Books by PETER FREUCHEN

•

ESKIMO

IVALU

ARCTIC ADVENTURE

IT'S ALL ADVENTURE

THE LAW OF LARION

VAGRANT VIKING

ICE FLOES AND FLAMING WATER

THE LEGEND OF DANIEL WILLIAMS

The Legend of Daniel Williams

by

PETER FREUCHEN

ROBERT HALE LIMITED
63 Old Brompton Road London S.W.7

First published in Great Britain 1958

Printed in Great Britain by
Lowe and Brydone (Printers) Limited, London, N.W.10

ACKNOWLEDGMENT

I wish to thank Theon Wright, Past President of The Adventurers' Club and a good friend, who helped me so generously with the many details of getting this story written and into print.

This Story is dedicated

to

Albert Lewin

as a token
of friendship and regard

FOREWORD

After the death of my wife in 1921, I left Greenland, where we had been living in the northern part of that cold and desolate country, and wandered down into Canada. Here I found myself among people of a warmer climate, where rivers had eaten through the mountains forming a vast and ragged upheaval, which was coated in the winter with ice and snow but covered over in the valleys with great forests. This land was inhabited by Indians and white trappers and traders, and by wolves and bears and, of course, fur-bearing animals, such as the fox, the marten, and the beaver.

It was the abundance of fur-bearing animals that brought the Hudson's Bay Company into being; and it was here in this tree-covered country below the Arctic Circle that I first encountered this great institution that stretches its arms from England to the Yukon; and also here that I first heard of Daniel Williams.

I mention them together because they are inseparably linked in my mind: the first, an organization of great scope and interests; and the other, a black outlaw of the forests, a huge Negro who had once been a slave and who seemed to have spread terror from the Slave Lakes to the Klondike.

Daniel Williams—or Nigger Dan, as he was called—had been dead many years before I arrived in this region. However, the Hudson's Bay Company still flourished, as it does today; and the men who worked for it were for the most part generous and loyal to "the Company," as it was called, and were highly skilled in trading with the Indians.

I had first heard of Daniel Williams in Hudson's Bay. Later when I traveled down through the Klondike and the Peace

River country, his name cropped up again and again. There were strange stories, or rather fragments of stories, about this huge black man, who was more of a legend than a fact—a black Paul Bunyan, powerful enough to fell a tree with a blow of his fist, it would seem, and with an uncanny knack of hitting anything he aimed at with a rifle.

He had once worked for the Hudson's Bay Company as a roustabout and camp cook at old Fort St. John, on the Peace River. Then he "went wild," as the old-timers put it, and lived with the Indians. For many years he seemed to have been a shadowy figure who roved through the forests, shooting miners and raiding trading posts. There was one story of an old French trader, Jacques Pardonet, whom he was reported to have robbed and murdered; at the same time he read from an old torn Bible to the Indians and sang hymns in a roaring, deeply musical voice.

One account told of his robbing a trading post of several bolts of white cotton cloth, later used to perform baptismal services for the Indians of the Beaver tribe. All these reports were so strange and fragmentary, and often so conflicting, that I found myself deeply interested; and, being young and eager and with little else to occupy me at the time, I dug into these fragments of stories.

There was a report of a Mr. W. F. Butler, for example; he was "Justice of the Peace for Rupert's Land and the Northwest." Rupert's Land was a name formerly used to describe the entire region in which the Hudson's Bay Company operated its trading posts and stores; and it was like saying "Justice of the Peace for the northern half of Canada"—an area of some two million square miles, two thirds the size of the United States, including Alaska!

Justice Butler, in one of his reports in the Hudson's Bay Company journal, told of this strange black bandit, Nigger Dan, who "came floating down the river; a solitary Negro—pioneer, cook, trapper, vagrant, idler, or squatter, as chance suited him."

It was a curious description; yet it was so vague and uncertain I could not permit my curiosity to rest at this point. So I asked many questions of the old-timers who had known of Nigger Dan when he was tried at Fort Saskatchewan for murder in the year 1880.

It was from one of these old-timers—a leathery old man, rather shruken, with gnarled hands and a frizzled white beard that covered his weather-beaten face in patches, like clumps of frosted grass on the tundra—that I learned some really curious things about Nigger Dan.

I met him at the trading post at Dunvegan, below Fort St. John on the Peace River. This was the place where Nigger Dan had committed most of his "crimes," and this old-timer not only had seen him but knew Banjo Mike MacGinney, about whom much had been written during the trial at Fort Saskatchewan.

The old-timer squinted at me from under the overhang of his gray, bristling brows, with a mixture of mirth and memories in the glint of his eyes; and he remarked:

"It was the Company that did him in."

I could not know how much of what the old-timer said was true and how much was a part of the fading fabric of an aging memory, but his remark struck me with surprise. I had always thought the opposite—that Nigger Dan had harassed the Company which had formerly employed him.

"You mean—the Company?" I finally asked. It was an inane question, but I could think of nothing else to say. It was startling that the old man blamed the Company.

He nodded, clawing with his fingers, that were like twigs, at the tangle of beard that covered the lower half of his face; and he grinned knowingly.

"He was tried for missin' the Company factor at Fort St. John with a rifle shot—by about two inches. Dan had been a slave, you know; come up from Georgia or Virginny or some such place, after Lincoln freed the slaves. But he warn't no slave up here!" The old-timer chuckled. "He only reckonized two masters—Queen Victoria and Jesus Christ! He was always writin' notes to one an' prayin' to the other."

9

The old man was no longer working at anything. He had been a trapper, part of the time for the Company. Now he was drifting about, and appeared to have nothing to gain or lose by what he said.

"You know, he warn't really tried for murder," he went on, still raking his fingers through his whiskers. "He was tried at Fort Saskatch' for shootin' at Mister King, the Company factor. That was where Banjo Mike come into it. He said, by God, if Nigger Dan missed Mister King's head by two inches, like they said, that was the best proof in the world he didn't aim to hit him. He said if Dan had wanted to kill him, he'd sure as hell have hit him . . . That's when they damn near threw Banjo Mike out of the courtroom, and near busted up the trial!"

It was this part of the story that interested me. I had found some ancient newspaper reports of the trial; and later I read some of the old records in the Municipal Library in New York City. But a search of all these records did not even show the names of the men Nigger Dan killed. There was much more written about how he almost killed the Hudson's Bay Company factor, Mr. W. C. King. There was also a copy of a letter he had written to another factor, George Kennedy, who preceded King at Fort St. John. He addressed this to "KENedy" and warned him to stay away from Dan Williams' "PREMEEis" —presumably his premises—"BEcos I sHALL Not BE Trub-BLED Nor TRod On oNLY By HER Most NoBEL MAJEsTY GovERNMENT."

The story of the white cotton cloth he took from the trading post of Jacques Pardonet, the Frenchman who was murdered, did more to establish the reputation of Dan Williams as an outlaw and wanton killer than anything, except possibly missing Mr. King's head by two inches. Nigger Dan wanted the cloth to "baptize" the Indians of the Beaver tribe with whom he lived for several years. This was construed by the court as inciting the Indians to uprisings; and it was in consequence a more serious offense than shooting the miners, even more heinous than murder, since it involved both robbery and revolt.

So I resolved to put together what I could find out about the story of Daniel Williams. The names may not all be the right ones; and in some cases the things that were actually said may have been different from what I have written, since there was no one to write them down at the time. But in the main it is the best I can make out of the mass of myths that have grown up around this great black outlaw of the northern woods.

There are many things in the story that came down by word of mouth, tales of miners and trappers, and things that were dimly remembered from earlier days when Dan Williams had been a slave. These, of course, were of no particular interest in the trial, and they certainly had no bearing on how close he came to shooting Mr. King. And none of these things will be found in the records of the case. Yet they are the parts of a man's life that should be pieced together—patched, if you will—until they form the fabric of things that really happened, even though they are fashioned from the simple fragments of memory, and perhaps an aging imagination like that of the old man at Dunvegan.

Since a story must begin somewhere—and I began my search into the old accounts of the trial at Fort Saskatchewan—it may be as well to start at that point, in March of 1880. . . .

The Legend
of
Daniel Williams

CHAPTER ONE

The spectators in the little courtroom at Fort Saskatchewan had not come to witness a trial, since the outcome was a foregone conclusion. They had come to see the strange, almost legendary black man who sat in the prisoner's box, his great bulk filling the railed enclosure. They came to watch him roll his eyes, like a wild animal; and to hear him mutter strange words: "Holy Jesus, Yo' gotta save Dan! Yo' Mother, Mary, done saved Yo', and now Yo' gotta save me. . . ."

These expressions of piety were almost blasphemous, considering the circumstances; and when he uttered the words, the spectators would sigh as a single person. It was as if the prisoner's queer conduct justified all that had been said of him —a giant black outlaw, who spread terror through the Canadian Northwest, frightening even the hardy people of that remote region.

In the dim light that filtered through the frosted windows on this chilly March day, the prisoner's heavy features—his coarse mouth and the ugly shape of his forehead and jaw— seemed to be almost grotesque to the writers who reported the trial. One wrote that the prisoner's "bestial expression" had shocked the townspeople who came to see the affair. There was an attitude of fixed hostility in the glances of the jurors; and toward the end of the trial this curious unfriendliness on the part of spectators as well as jurors seemed to increase rather than diminish. One of the news accounts reported—with the pardonable exaggeration of a journalist trying to make his point—that the courtroom was "hushed with horror" as the final stages of the Crown's case were unfolded.

The final witness for the Crown was on the stand, a red-jacketed constable of the Canadian Mounted Police. He had taken his place in the square-backed witness chair and was explaining, with the aid of a drawing, exactly where the bullet had lodged in the framework of the door, near Mr. King's head. It was at this point that the prisoner suddenly roared out, in a deep, musical voice:

"Jesus save me! Ef'n I'd wanted to shoot Mister King, I'd sure have hit him, Mister Judge. Dan don' miss nothin' he shoots at—not nothin'!" His white-rimmed eyes scanned the room, and his heavy lips parted in a slight grin which exposed his white teeth. "I jes' wanted to scare him up a bit," he said.

The spectators looked at the prisoner and even the judge seemed to be aroused from his judicial calm. He struck the gavel sharply several times, according to the reports of the proceedings; then he admonished the prisoner that this sort of conduct would do him no good. "The defendant will have an opportunity to present evidence at the proper time," he remarked. The black prisoner said nothing further but rolled his eyes toward the ceiling and muttered: "Jesus, Yo' gotta save me!"

The black man sank back in his chair, his great head rolling from side to side, his heavy lips twisted in a momentary smile that showed the white flash of his teeth. It was almost an apologetic smile; but the effect, with his thick lips and heavy jaw, was to give him a fearsome expression. The spectators stared in fascination at this legendary man, whose name was used by mothers in western Canada to frighten their children into behaving—"Be good, or Nigger Dan will get you!"

Most of Dan Williams' story had already been told; but the judge was an honest and conscientious man, and he patiently explained to the prisoner that he would be accorded his full rights, even to the extent of being allowed to tell his story after the Crown had presented its case. Thus far, no one had made much sense of his rambling exclamations, least of all the jurors who sat in bored, humorless silence. Most of them were busy men, traders or small businessmen with enterprises that needed their constant attention. The tedious effort of the Crown to present all the details of the case, even to such an insignificant matter as the distance by which Dan Williams' bullet had missed the factor's head, annoyed them—particularly since there was only one possible outcome of the trial. What defense could a man have who had tried to kill the Hudson's Bay factor, Mr. King, and had shot down in cold blood two of the constables who tried to arrest him?

They had listened with growing indifference as Constable Gladwyn, the last witness, pointed to a small cross he had drawn on the sketch, marking the place where Nigger Dan's bullet hit the doorway.

"That's where it hit," he said, and the press noted the "firmness of his tone."

"Now you would say, Mr. Gladwyn," the prosecutor asked, adjusting his thick-lensed glasses to the precarious bridge of his long, thin nose, "you would say that the fact that the bullet missed Mr. King by a distance of—perhaps two inches——" The prosecutor smirked magnanimously; it had been established that the bullet was only one and five-eighths inches from Mr. King's head, which was against the door frame when the shot was fired. "You would say he was trying to shoot Mr. King?"

The constable nodded, and was apparently on the point of elaborating on this conclusion when another interruption occurred, this time from the rear of the room. One of the bailiffs spoke up:

"Banjo Mike is here, your Worship . . . He says he's got something to say."

The judge frowned. He had probably been mentally summing up what he planned to say to the jury, and these interruptions were onerous. Any interruption was onerous. The Crown had presented its facts, and they were plain and incontrovertible: Dan Williams, a notorious outlaw whose crimes had outraged authorities throughout the Western Provinces, and particularly the Hudson's Bay Company—whose factor, Mr. W. C. King, he had tried to shoot—this outlaw had at

B 17

last been brought to the bar of justice. He had shot down two constables while resisting lawful arrest; and in addition—as was clearly established at the trial—he had looted trading posts, aroused unrest among the Indians, and had become obnoxious to the Hudson's Bay Company, an offense that in many ways was more serious than murder. And if further proof of Dan Williams' villainy were needed, it was furnished in his conduct during the trial—a black man blasphemously insisting that he was a "messenger of the Lord" and even attempting, as was testified in the trial, to perform heathenish rites of baptism in the waters of the Peace River when he was living among the Indians.

The judge had given all reasonable attention to Dan Williams' rights, under the concept of legal safeguards peculiar to British justice. While it was true that defense counsel had not been provided—since there actually was no need for it— the judge had used his own good judicial temperance to assure a fair trial. He had even been lenient with the prisoner's frequent appeals to "the Lord Jesus," which were sacrilegious and even downright blasphemous and none of it, of course, material to the case.

Now there was this new interruption.

Banjo Mike moved up the aisle between the rows of benches in the rear of the courtroom, and stood within a few feet of the judge. He was a broad, squat man, with a short, bristling reddish beard which covered the lower half of his face and merged with his hair, so that his twinkling blue eyes looked like twin lakes in an autumn forest.

"Please state your reason for interrupting this proceeding," the judge said, with an even sharper tone than was customary. He was old in the service of justice and disliked anything that interfered with the orderly dignity of a courtroom.

"I'm Mike MacGinney, your Majesty," Banjo Mike said. He paused to wave at the prisoner, who was grinning with unabashed delight. "I been up tradin' on the Peace River, an' I come four hundred mile to find out what in hell you people are tryin' to do to my friend Dan!"

18

The judge rapped his gavel on the bench.

"You will please use proper language when you are addressing this court, Mr. MacGinney. And may I also remind you that you are addressing the Crown's Court—not the Crown."

Banjo Mike stood solidly on both feet. His bristling face was twisted into an ingratiating smile, but his blue eyes watched the judge warily.

"Sure, your Majesty . . . Hell, that ain't cussin'! You should of heard Left-handed Jim when I fetched him a crack on the head with a shovel the time he knocked Dan down for shootin' up the damn miners."

Banjo Mike was too old in the trader's game not to understand the value of diversionary tactics. He suddenly turned toward the prisoner:

"I'd like to shake hands with Dan, if it ain't against the dignity of this court, your Majesty."

Without waiting for approval, Banjo Mike strode across to the prisoner's box and held out his hand. Dan grasped it. The spectators craned forward in sudden anticipation of a break in the monotony of the trial.

"Jesus—He done sent yo', Mister Banjo!" the giant black man shouted, grinning and rolling his eyes. "He knows Dan ain't done nothin'——"

Banjo Mike slapped him on the shoulder, and turned toward the judge.

"Hell, your Majesty—you can settle this in five minutes! You heard that constable feller, Mr. Gladwyn, tell you Dan missed Mr. King by two inches. If Dan wanted to kill that damn fool King, he'd be a dead Scotchman today and not sittin' in this courtroom!"

The judge banged his gavel, but Banjo Mike began to warm up.

"Let me tell you this, your Majesty—every gold digger, every trader, every Indian within two hundred mile of Fort St. John knows Dan Williams can knock the eye out of a rabbit on the dead run at three hundred yards. Every time he shoots, he can do that. I seen him shoot a duck through the eye once when it was flyin', your Majesty—with a rifle, by God!"

The judge had half risen from his seat

"Mike MacGinney, you canna' come into this courtroom and testify as you wish. This is a court of law—and ye've not been sworn as a witness. The proper procedures will be observed— and once again, Mr. MacGinney, you are addressing the Crown's Court, not the Crown!"

Banjo Mike waved a conciliatory hand.

"Sure, your Majesty—but like I said——"

"Ye'll be silent!" the judge screamed, forgetting judicial temperament for the moment. "Bide your time, Mike Mac-Ginney—if ye've got something to say, ye can say it at the proper time. But ye canna' come barging into this courtroom without so much as a by-your-leave——"

Banjo Mike pulled out a red handkerchief and blew his nose, which effectively drowned out the judge's remarks. He was known to everyone within five hundred miles of Fort Saskatchewan as a "free trader"; that is, a trader who was not in the employ of the Hudson's Bay Company. He was shrewd and canny; and he knew the environs of Fort Saskatchewan were not friendly territory for him. He eyed the judge speculatively over the folds of his handkerchief.

The jurors were looking at him, considerably impressed by his recital of Nigger Dan's prowess with a rifle. It was said that this black outlaw had never missed a shot; and here was tangible proof, added confirmation, as it were, that the giant Negro in the prisoner's box was a killer of legendary proportions.

"Like I said, your Majesty," Banjo Mike went on, "if Dan wanted to shoot Mr. W. C. King, you can bet all the gold in the Klondike that Mr. King wouldn't be here to tell about it!" He turned to face the jury, warmed with the enthusiasm of his own oratory. "By God, I'll tell you somethin' else!" The judge's gavel banged with the full impact of judicial ire, but Banjo Mike had a full head of steam. "I been with Dan when them damn miners was shootin' at him—and Dan never shot anybody that wasn't shootin' at him! And by God, when he shot, he hit what he was shootin' at!"

The last rap of the gavel brought the bailiff. He took a firm grip on Banjo Mike's arm.

The judge looked sternly at Banjo Mike.

"Mr. Bailiff, you will escort Mike MacGinney from the courtroom and place him in custody. I will dispose of his case later."

"Dispose, hell!" Banjo Mike roared. He tried to shake off the restraining grip of the bailiff while several others moved close to lend what assistance might be necessary. "You want the truth, your Majesty, and by God——"

Another voice, deep and booming, chimed into the discordant shouting, even above the banging of the judge's gavel. Dan, stirred by the first friendly words he had heard since he was brought down weeks before from Fort St. John, on the Peace River, rose to his feet and lifted his great hands toward the ceiling.

"That's right, Banjo," he shouted, his voice carrying through the courtroom in an awesome roar. "I thank Yo', Jesus! Yo' brought Banjo to tell these folks the truth——"

Dan tried to lift one leg over the railing of the prisoner's box, but the entire official complement of the courtroom descended on him, with the exception of His Worship, the magistrate. Banjo Mike was left alone for the moment, and he continued to shout at the magistrate, who continued to rap with his gavel. Within a few minutes order was restored.

Dan Williams offered no further resistance when the bailiff shoved him back into the prisoner's box. The trial was immediately adjourned until the following day, when Banjo Mike was ordered, under pain of arrest, to appear for the disposal of his case.

When Banjo Mike appeared the next morning, he was warned that a violent outburst, such as he had introduced into the calm decorum of the court, might well be construed as an insult to the dignity of the Crown itself, punishable by fine and imprisonment.

Banjo Mike said nothing, but he looked over at the prisoner,

21

who sat in silence, apparently subdued by the misfortune that had befallen his friend. The old trader may have thought of many things at that moment—of the day he led the miners across the Peace River to rescue Dan from the Indians; or he may have thought of the night he and Donald Ross, the factor, led Dan down to the river and helped him escape; or of the many times he voyaged with Dan along the Peace River, Dan paddling the canoe and doing all the camp chores . . . But he said nothing further that is of record in the trial.

"The court will take cognizance of yer trade and yer calling, Mike MacGinney," the judge said. "Ye're a wild and untamed man, with an affinity for those that are also wild and untamed. No further action will be taken against ye, providin' ye remain calm and peaceful and take no further part in these proceedings."

The judge's gavel lent emphasis to this decision, and the intervention of Mike MacGinney judicially was a closed incident.

There was no further evidence to be offered, and the prosecutor quickly closed the Crown's case. The judge asked Daniel Williams if he had anything to present, but the prisoner merely sat with his head bent forward, and made no reply. This was taken as an affirmative answer to all the charges presented by the Crown.

The prosecutor, in his summation to the jury, took the occasion to compliment His Worship, the magistrate, for his decisive handling of the unprecedented situation that had arisen when Banjo Mike came "forcing his way into the courtroom—for what reason? To speak for this killer!"

He pointed a thin finger at Dan, who still did not look up.

"It was as if the barbarism of this man—the spirit of lawlessness itself—had invaded the very court where he was on trial. And in the midst of this disorder, the calm dignity of British justice asserted itself. It was like an admonition—an omen, if you please—to you, gentlemen of the jury!"

This oratory, of course, was unnecessary; but it provided a fine ending to the case, and gave the prosecutor, a rather wizened man who usually had only routine crimes to prosecute, an opportunity to satisfy a flare for the dramatic.

With the prosecutor's stirring admonition ringing in their ears, the jurors received into their hands on the twelfth day of March, in the year 1880, the fate of Nigger Dan Williams.

CHAPTER TWO

There were few old-timers along the Peace River who remembered where Dan Williams came from or when he came to Canada. He first appeared at Fort Vermilion, with his friend Joe Potter, in the early 1870's. Both were good cooks and handy men to have around; black as coal, one towering a head above his fellows, the other short and wide-shouldered. Both were as strong as a bull moose. Nigger Dan was probably the best rifle shot in Northwest Canada.

Few men who traveled the gold trails knew much about the origin of those who traveled with them. A man was simply a man, walking beside other men over the rough, hard trails, sleeping and working and sometimes fighting. It was only when a man did something notable, such as finding gold or killing another man, that he became important; but this seldom carried into his past.

It was evident from the beginning that neither Nigger Dan nor Nigger Joe was a miner. They worked on the gravel beds along the Peace River only when they were "hired" to help another miner; and they almost never were paid for this labor. Dan and Joe, for their part, said little about where they came from. Perhaps they remembered little; or possibly in the hard months of travel, up from Port Arthur on Lake Superior, across the wilderness of lakes to the Slave River country, and thence along the Peace River to Fort Vermilion and to Dunvegan and Fort St. John, they had learned by experience that white men did not care much about where black men came from.

And since there was not much for either to remember with pleasure, the past had faded behind them. Even their wives, back in the hot, soft land of Georgia, were only shadowy fig-

24

ures on the fringe of their memory . . . like the tall white man from the North who had stood bareheaded under the oak tree that spread over the little white country church where colored folk went to worship and sing hymns, and had told them about the blessings of "freedom." But this had happened long before Dan and Joe came to Saskatchewan, and neither of them could have remembered very much about it if anyone had asked—which no one did.

Dan later recalled the white man's talking about "freedom," and it seemed to be something like heaven. The old preacher, the Reverend Sam, had stood beside the white man, his bald, black head glistening in the sun that slanted through the great branches of the tree and the white fringe of hair around his head making it look like a giant cotton berry. The Reverend Sam nodded at intervals, as if he understood, more than the others, what the white man was saying about "freedom." Now and then he would mutter "Amen!" When he did this, Dan would always nod and say "Amen!" too. It was for this reason, more than anything else, that Dan knew "freedom" had the blessing of the Lord.

This had happened many years ago—so many years that neither Dan nor Joe could have said whether it was three years, or five, or even ten; but Dan remembered one thing very well: he had been terribly hungry most of the time, because all the food had been taken by the "Lincoln soldiers" and most of the white folks on the plantation had gone away and some had been killed or had forgotten to come back.

For a while there was enough food, so that the colored folk could live by stealing a little here and there; but later there was no food to steal. The colored folk sat around, crying and praying; then a few remembered what the white man from the North had said about "freedom."

One day Joe Potter spoke to Dan about this.

"Ev'ybody is free up in the No'th," he told Dan. "Tha's what the white folks say, an' Reveren' Sam, he say the same thing. We gotta go no'th, Dan, where folks is free an' where we can get somethin' to eat!"

25

Dan agreed with this philosophy. His belly was empty and he was beginning to feel mean. He and Joe went to see the Reverend Sam, and the old preacher verified what Joe had said. "Yo' is now free men, jus' like white folks," he told Dan. "Nobody has gotten the right to tell yo' what you gotta do, lessen it's for wages."

Dan and Joe asked the Reverend Sam what "wages" were. The old man frowned and rubbed the top of his bald head; finally he told them that wages might be as much as ten cents, particularly in the North where the white folks had lots of money. Neither Dan nor Joe had ever had ten cents, so they both went to their wives and explained that they were "goin' No'th."

Some time later Dan and Joe were put aboard a wagon driven by a white man. They were told that they were going north to work for wages on farms up in Ohio. They had no idea where Ohio was, or why they were going—except that it was part of the "freedom" they had been promised.

The next few months were vague in the memories of both Dan and Joe. They remembered that the wagon in which they rode was pretty well filled with colored men; and there was a lot of laughing and hand-waving by their wives and the other colored people on the plantation when they left. But neither Dan nor Joe felt very happy as they watched the yellow road curving away behind them and saw the familiar spreading oak trees where they had played as boys fading away into the dust.

As the wagon jolted northward, Dan and Joe felt less and less happy about things; finally they stopped talking and stared at the country as it rolled by. At night they stopped at farmhouses, where the white man arranged for food; and they slept in the wagon or under it, depending on who got there first.

They finally reached Ohio, and at a small town they were told to get out. There were a lot of white men around, staring at them; and Dan heard one man say, "I'll take that big buck nigger." Late that day Dan was taken to a farm with two other colored boys and put to work in a field, breaking rocks.

It was harder work than any they had done down in Georgia. In the daytime they were fed from buckets of food which a white farmhand brought in a wagon, and in the evening they ate at a long table set up in a large shed, where they also slept.

On Saturday night Dan was told that there would be no work on Sunday. He was given some money, which he carefully rolled up in his handkerchief. This was his "wages." Several of the farmhands had hitched up a wagon and were setting out for town. They signaled to Dan to climb into the wagon and go along.

It was a small town with a wide market place, or square, in the center; and Dan found himself with several colored men, pushing his way along the edge of a brick-paved street. He heard someone call his name, and he saw Joe coming across the street.

Joe said he had been taken to another farm and put to work clearing fields. He had also been told there would be no work on Sundays, and had been given his wages.

"How much wages yo' got?" Joe asked.

Dan had not counted his wages—from which the farmer had taken some money for food and board—so he pulled out the handkerchief and unrolled it. With the aid of Joe, he counted the money and found that it added up to two dollars. This was more than Joe had recevied, but Joe told Dan the farmer had kept more of his wages so he could have it when his work was finished.

For some time Dan and Joe wandered along the board sidewalk, peering into taverns where people seemed to be drinking and having a good time. Most of these places were full of white people, and they did not go in. Finally they saw some colored men in a room and decided this was the place to go.

A man looked them over when they came in and asked if they had any money. This was strange, because in Georgia colored folks didn't have money. If one man had a bottle, everybody drank out of it until it was empty. Then they either went looking for somebody else with a bottle or dropped off to sleep.

27

The man who spoke to them explained to Dan and Joe that they must pay money to drink. Since they now had money, they immediately pushed it across a bar to the man who was pouring drinks, and he poured several short glasses full of whisky.

Dan and Joe drank the whisky, grinning at each other. It was plain to see that "freedom" was going to be very pleasant. After a while a few men began to sing, and Dan—whose voice was deep and strong—joined in, although he did not know any of the songs. Finally the man who was pouring drinks told them they had no more money, and they were shoved into the street.

"You've had enough, boys," he told them. "Can't have trouble here with you black fellows. Get out!"

A white man who had been standing in the road watching them came up to Dan and Joe. He knew a place where they could get some more whisky, he said, and led them by the arm to the place, a short distance away. This was down by the river, and the man took them into a room where two men were sitting at a table.

One of the men at the table explained that they were hiring men to work on an ore boat then in port at Lorain, on the shore of Lake Erie. It was going across the lake to a Canadian port. Neither Dan nor Joe was able to do much talking, each having had about twenty drinks of whisky, so they merely nodded.

Things were fairly vague for the rest of the night, but in the morning Dan awakened to find himself looking up at a few faint stars that still dotted the morning sky. He was lying on his back on a floor, and the floor seemed to be moving under him. It was cold—much colder than it had ever been down in Georgia.

He rolled over and saw that Joe was sleeping near him. Several other men were sleeping on the wooden floor, and from the clanking going on around him Dan decided there was some kind of machine working nearby.

Dan stared for some time at the sky, wondering, and then

realized he was on a boat. He realized too that it was much bigger than any boat he had ever been on before, although he had been to Savannah as a boy and had seen the great boats come in from the sea.

"Glory be!" he muttered, and then rolled to his knees and held his clasped hands in front of him. "Oh, Jesus, I been a sinner! I has got drunk an' sick!" He groaned, and this awakened Joe, who sat blinking in the dim, cold light of the early dawn.

Dan and Joe worked two voyages on the big ore boat, spending two days ashore each time the boat reached port, and using what money they had for drinking. Joe also bought a few small gifts, such as handkerchiefs for the girls he managed to flush up in each port. These were colored girls; neither Joe nor Dan would have dreamed of associating with white girls. They had seen men beaten to death just for looking at a white woman, and there was nothing in their new "freedom" that served to erase these memories from their minds. When one of the white girls in the drinking places looked straight at Dan, her red lips curving in a bright smile, he pulled at Joe's arm and they got out of the place as fast as they could.

After the second trip across the lake, Dan spoke to Joe about something that was troubling his mind.

"We ain't goin' No'th any mo', Joe," he said. "This here boat jes' keeps goin' up an' down the lake—an' it never gets no place!"

Joe nodded. He told Dan he was sick of the stench of the galley; down in the belly of the ship behind the engine room the heat and the clank of the engines and the rancid odors of the ship's stores were more unbearable than the hottest day in the fields back in Georgia. He wanted to get off the ship.

They visited a tavern near the ship's dock, and asked the bartender if there were any other boats going north. He gave them a sharp look, then signaled a white man who sat at one of the tables drinking alone. The man rose and came over.

"A couple of bully boys wantin' to go north," he said. "Can you fix 'em up, mate?"

29

The white man was broad-chested and powerfully built, with several days' growth of whiskers that gave his features a mean expression. He looked over the two colored men. Then he nodded and motioned for them to follow him.

Dan and Joe soon found themselves on another boat, and this time they were traveling through a deep, narrow channel past several big islands. The wind was cold, biting through their cotton shirts. They finally reached a port town on the American side of the Canadian border, and were glad to go ashore, where they quickly headed for the warmth of a tavern. Here they found another bartender who told them about another ship, which took them across Lake Superior to a place called Port Arthur.

After inquiring among the other members of the crew whether this ship would go farther north, Dan and Joe were told that this was impossible: they were as far north as the ships could sail.

"We is goin' to leave this ship," Dan announced to Joe, quite firmly. "We got mo'n ten dollahs, which is mo'n all the white folks in Ge'oja got, Joe. As long as we keep goin' No'th, we can live like white folks—an' ef'n we go back South again, we ain't goin' to find any freedom."

Joe was impressed by this sudden reckoning of their wealth. He was ready to leave the ship anyway, since he always drew the job in the ship's galley, but Dan worked on deck. They found the mate and told him they wanted to get off, and since the ore boat was returning with a light load, the mate readily agreed.

Dan and Joe once more headed for a tavern near the waterfront. This, they had found, was the best way to get information about a place. They had learned by this time that bartenders were always a ready source of local knowledge. They also found that in the atmosphere of a saloon—particularly as they got farther north—there was less attention paid to color, and more to their money.

"We is goin' No'th," Dan told the bartender, a small, amiable man wearing a shiny celluloid collar and black tie over a bib of white apron. He seemed quite different from the bartenders at the other end of the Great Lakes, and when he spoke Dan realized that he spoke differently.

"Mon Dieu! Thees *ees* nort'!" the man exclaimed, with a flash of very white teeth. Dan grinned. It always made him feel better when a man smiled, even if he did not understand a word said. It showed the man was friendly.

"You got any wagons goin' up No'th?" Dan asked. "We's worked on wagons as well as boats."

The bartender smiled, and beckoned to a man in a red shirt and black hat. "Thees gentlemen weesh to go nort'," the bartender said, and the red-shirted man took Dan and Joe by the arm.

He led them to a table, and took some papers from his pocket.

"You come to the right place," he said. His eyes were black and sharp, but his smile was also good-natured and friendly. Dan nodded to everything the man said. He had learned to agree with those who talked with him; in that way no one would get angry, and Dan knew that whenever a white man and a colored man got angry, the colored man always got the worst of anything that happened.

He looked over Dan and Joe from head to foot; then he explained that he had papers which would allow them to go anywhere in Canada, provided they were employed by the company which he represented.

"Can you write?" the man asked. Dan nodded, but Joe said nothing. It depended, of course, upon what the man asked them to write. Dan could write his name and a few words of prayer that he had copied from the Bible. Joe couldn't write.

The man pushed a piece of paper in front of each.

"Write your name," he said.

Dan took a steel pen which the man handed him, after dipping it in a bottle carried in his pocket, and spelled out in capital letters: DANIEL WILLIAMS.

Joe was unable to write his name. Dan helped and soon the

two papers were signed. The man folded them and put them into his pocket.

"Be here at four o'clock in the morning," he said. "You both got jobs with the Hudson's Bay Company." He looked at the two men and then added: "Be sure you're here on time, lads —you're citizens of the British Crown now, and as long as you work for the Company, nobody can do a damn thing to you!"

The man said his name was Eli, and as a binder to the agreement Dan and Joe had just signed, he gave each a dollar.

"You have a contract with the Queen," Eli said, and although Dan did not understand what the man was talking about, he grinned and nodded.

"We is goin' to find a gal I seen down on the dock," Joe said, rising from his chair, his face still beaming. Dan felt embarrassed. Joe always paid more attention than a God-fearing man should to things having to do with women.

Eli frowned, and asked Dan where they were going.

"We ain't goin' no place, boss massa," Dan said, apologetically. "Jes' down by de wha'f. We is goin' to be heah at fo' o'clock, like yo' said."

The red-shirted man took the papers from his pocket and pointed to the signature in heavy black ink.

"You boys got jobs with the Company," he said. "You signed a contract with the Queen—and this is her signature! You've promised to work for the Company for five years, and if you don't want police trouble, lads, you'd better be here! We don't like deserters up in this country."

There was a hard edge to his voice, and Dan noticed that his eyes were not as friendly as they had been. Dan looked at Joe, and Joe looked at Dan.

"No, sir, we ain't goin' nowhere," Dan said, and they both sat down. Finally Eli showed them to a back room, where they slept on the floor.

The next morning Dan and Joe were given heavy clothes, with strong boots which did not fit too well, but which were much better than the old shoes they had worn. Dan was put to work loading the wagons and Joe helped round up the mules that were to haul the wagons a thousand miles to the west. By daylight the big wagons were creaking through the deserted street of the port city, heading out toward the green wilderness to the north.

The road, hardly discernible in places, wound through rough uplands into a country called the Rainy River country, then out along wide flat plains, and finally into a great wooded land studded with hundreds of lakes.

It was unlike any country either Dan or Joe had ever seen before: a wild region covered with dense forests through which the road turned in seemingly endless curves. They passed through several large towns, stopping only long enough to load fresh supplies of food for the men and mules.

At a place called McMurray they turned north into colder country, heading along a straight placid river that Dan learned would lead them to the Slave River country.

Dan and Joe went to Eli, who rode a horse at the head of the line of wagons.

"What's this Slave River country?" Dan asked. "Yo' all ain't got no slaves up heah, has yo'?"

Eli laughed, and then regarded Dan with some curiosity. "You were a slave?" he asked.

Dan nodded. "Ain't all colored folks workin' now for white folks?" he asked.

Eli shrugged. Dan tried to explain what the white man from the North had told the colored folks in Georgia, about colored folks everywhere in the world being made free by Abraham Lincoln; but Eli showed little interest.

"Ef'n yo' got some slave country up heah, we ain't goin' on," Dan said. "Me an' Joe is goin' to go back."

Dan stood still, not knowing whether to expect a blow for his sudden defiance. Eli looked at the two black men and laughed. There was a hard sound to his laugh that made Dan think of the overseer, back on the plantation in Georgia, and he braced himself for a blow. But none came.

"Get back to work," Eli said, abruptly. "You're getting

wages as long as you work. But don't get any ideas about going back!"

At night they camped on the riverbank, squatting around the fires which the roustabouts built, fighting mosquitoes. Sometimes small animals crept into the camps, and there was always a lively skirmish with a lot of cursing. Dan knew in general what these words meant, and he always felt bad when anyone spoke in a rough way about God or Jesus. He would take out his Bible and try to make out words in the flickering light of the campfire which would enable him to explain to these folks the beautiful words of Jesus.

"He don' like sinnin' even in the woods out heah," he told the men. They laughed and referred to him after that as "the nigger Sky Pilot."

Dan seldom got into an argument, except to help out Joe, who was always getting into some kind of trouble. When Joe got into a fight, he always got beaten, since it was obviously not possible for him to fight back. Down on the plantation in Georgia the few colored men who did fight back were fearful examples to the rest of the colored folk, making them understand clearly the law that said a black man who hit a white man must be killed. So Dan and Joe took their beatings, and tried to keep from being hurt too much.

One day a man walking in the line behind Joe tried to trip him, so that the big pack Joe was carrying would become unbalanced and carry him over the edge of a steep bank. Joe dropped his pack and swung his fist at the other man. The blow caught the man by surprise, and he fell forward and lay still.

Dan had seen the thing happen, and he pushed forward and stood over Joe, who was panting, his eyes turning from side to side so that the whites showed in the blackness of his face. Dan was frightened, but he said nothing. The other men had stopped and they stood looking at the man who had been knocked down. Eli came up and asked a few questions.

The fellow on the ground rolled over and looked up, rubbing

34

his hand along the side of his jaw. Eli prodded him with the toe of his heavy boot.

"Don't pull another like that!" he snapped. "Come on—get moving! The next man that starts a fight in line will fight me, too!"

The men glanced at Joe with no little surprise, and Dan noticed that there was much less roughness after that.

It suddenly dawned on Dan that this was the "freedom" they were looking for. Here in the North a colored man could knock down a white man, and no one beat him to death for it.

"Thank Yo', Jesus!" he murmured in his prayers. "Yo' done sent Dan an' Joe to the place where the Lord has made ev'ybody free! Yo' done kep' your promise, Jesus, an' Dan gonna work for Yo' all his livin' days!"

Dan and Joe began to feel more comfortable among white folks.

McMurray had been the last town of any size they struck before heading along a wagon road that ran beside the river. Finally they came to a trading post where they transferred into big York boats, shifting cargo from the wagons to boats. Dan found out, by asking questions, that they were now on a water route all the way to Fort Vermilion, where the cargo would be stored by the Company.

Dan was even more useful in the boats than in the wagons. His powerful arms and shoulders pulled the big sweeps easily and without fatigue, his massive body working forward and backward in a steady rhythm. Now and then he broke out into a song, usually a hymn of comfort to colored folks, and his powerful voice rolled across the river.

Within a few weeks they pushed out into a big lake, where heavy winds drove the cold spray into their backs, soaking their thick woolen clothes. The men pulled harder on the oars, until they reached the shelter of the northern shore where a broad river emptied into the lake.

"This is the Peace River," Eli told the men. "Fort Vermilion is about six days upriver, and that's where ye'll be paid off for the trip. Some of you men'll stay on with the Company

35

at Vermilion. The rest will return with stuff we're takin' out."

He looked at Dan and Joe.

"Ain't no reason for you boys to come back," he said cheerfully. "We're takin' a few old hands back—men that's been up here a couple o' years. The company'll take care of you boys at Vermilion."

Dan and Joe did not know exactly what Eli meant, but they understood they would stay in the North, and would not have to go back. Dan liked this idea; it was just what he and Joe wanted. And so Dan Williams—who was now Nigger Dan to the roustabouts of the Hudson's Bay Company—headed toward Fort Vermilion and the lands of the Beaver Indians.

CHAPTER THREE

"The Company," at Fort Vermilion, was Mr. MacFarlane, the district manager. He was a tall man, with high cheekbones and a raw, wind-scuffed face that made him look perpetually peeved and uncomfortable; and his disposition went with his face.

He looked Dan and Joe over thoroughly and skeptically. They were the first black men who had come into that region, and although Mr. MacFarlane was not unaware of the existence of colored people, he was unfamiliar with them. And by nature and habit, he was not a man who enjoyed unfamiliar things.

"What do ye ken o' the way o' tradin' for hides?" he asked Dan. Not understanding what was meant, Dan grinned, apologetically and expansively. MacFarlane grunted; and by this simple process of job evaluation Dan Williams and Joe Potter became expendable in the Hudson's Bay Company's scheme of things at Fort Vermilion.

When the Reverend Davidson, a traveling minister of the Presbyterian faith, came to Mr. MacFarlane a few days later and suggested that the Company permit him to employ the services of Daniel Williams and Joe Potter as handymen on an evangelistic excursion into the surrounding Indian country, Mr. MacFarlane acquiesced, charging it up to his natural indulgence in matters of faith, and at the same time quite satisfied at the fortuitous circumstance which had permitted him to gracefully drop the colored members of his retinue from the payroll.

Dan was not a Presbyterian, but his faith was elastic. He

knew that he had not rendered the full devotion due the Lord Jesus on his travels to the North. There had been few churches and lapses of many days between prayers. At several of the ports along the Great Lakes he had suffered a lapse of more than prayer, chiefly because Joe was an even frailer reed than himself. And now there was this opportunity of serving a man of the cloth, however dissident his faith. It was in Dan's mind further proof that the Lord Jesus was watching over him.

The Reverend Davidson was a scrupulous taskmaster. He insisted that his camps be kept tidy and clean. He hardly spoke to his two handymen, except to give instructions; but he knew the ways of the woods, and Dan and Joe soon learned these ways because they had no other choice.

One day he handed Dan a gun.

"Can ye shoot?" he asked. Dan gazed at the rifle, a long-barreled breach-loading Sharps. As a boy, he had used a short-barreled shotgun, loading it with bits of nails from the muzzle, and had killed opossum down in the woods of the plantation in Georgia. But he had never shot a gun as beautiful as this.

The Reverend Davidson showed Dan how to load the gun, slipping the cartridge into the firing chamber; he indicated a tree stump perhaps two hundred yards away.

"Take guid aim at yon woodie," the missionary said. "If ye suppose it's a beastie, ye'll hit it—if ye can shoot! Mind, ye don't shake your hands when ye shoot. The bullets aren't to be had for nothing—even for a man o' God, like mysel'!"

Dan lined up the tree and fired. He knew he hit the tree stump because he had aimed at it. He handed the rifle back to the Reverend Davidson. They walked over to the tree and found the bullet hole. It was exactly in the middle of the stump.

The Reverend Davidson nodded with satisfaction. Dan thereafter became the provider for the camp, making short excursions into the woods for meat. The Reverend Davidson at first gave him a half-dozen shells, and Dan came back with five good bullets and one deer. Dan always came back with either the bullets or an animal for each bullet missing, and the

Reverend Davidson finally reduced his allotments of bullets to two for each trip. The second bullet was for use in case Dan shot a small animal, such as a rabbit.

About this time a group of miners were starting up the Peace River in quest of gold, which was said to abound in the lower reaches of the Rockies, many hundreds of miles to the west. Mr. MacFarlane's business was to make money for the Company, but money was made on the sale of furs which the Company traders got from the Indians, not from gold dug out of the ground. And it followed that men who spent their time looking for gold in the ground not only were wasting their efforts and time, but they did not fit in with the scheme of things. They were not "good business" for the Hudson's Bay Company.

Donald Ross, the factor at one of the upper river posts near a bend in the river called Fort St. John, had come down to Vermilion on company business and was about to set out for his post. Mr. MacFarlane graciously offered the services of Ross to take the gold prospectors up the river beyond the bend, and—as Mr. MacFarlane hoped—well out of the country.

Dan and Joe were assigned to accompany as helpers; and it was Mr. MacFarlane's fervent wish that they, too, would go up beyond the bend and out of the country. He had no valid objections to black men in the service of the Company, but it was slightly odd, and Mr. MacFarlane disliked anything that was even slightly odd.

Dan's marksmanship made him the general provider of meat for the party. Joe cooked for Ross and did odd jobs around the camp. Both became more or less indispensable members of the entourage as handymen and roustabouts.

It was in this way that Dan found himself headed into the wilderness in search of freedom—and into the land where the Beaver Indians lived. It also happened to be the country where Banjo Mike MacGinney did his trading, along the bend of the Peace River, above Fort St. John.

Men who had come back across the mountains from British Columbia and as far north as the Klondike had told of rich strikes. Many of the gold hunters who had gathered in Fort Vermilion knew little or nothing about mining, but they knew a great deal about gold. This was a wild country, covered with rivers that ran in strange directions, draining for the most part into the frozen tundras of the north. Great stretches of this vast country, spread over with lakes and mountains in tumbled, illogical confusion, had been invaded only by Indians and trappers.

Most of the men camped on the lower bend of the Peace River had not the slightest notion where they were; if they had suspected that Indians were lurking in the vicinity, they would have roared in raucous disdain. The experienced prospectors in the party, which had moved upstream from Fort Vermilion in the early spring thaw, were too few in number to influence the conduct of the majority; and they stayed by themselves, worked the creeks carefully for signs of "the yellow stuff," and kept a cautious eye out for signs of Indians.

Banjo Mike had joined the gold-hunting party because he saw an opportunity for trading with men who might have gold but would not be shrewd enough to know how to keep it. Banjo Mike knew the Indians and traded well with them, with full knowledge of how to get the best of the skins that the Indians traded for tobacco, knives, and fabrics.

He also knew most of the trappers in the area. They were lonely men who disliked populated areas, preferring to live their quiet lives in the woods. The sight of even a score of people settled around a trading post drove them back into the wilderness. Free traders, like Mike MacGinney, brought to these trappers tools and small supplies, such as needles and salt and medicine, and traded them for pelts.

A trapper can never get rich by his own efforts; whatever he catches in his traps, he must trade for supplies in order to go on catching animals in his traps. He is the natural prey of the free traders, and Banjo Mike was one of the best.

Banjo Mike's trading techniques with the Indians were far different from his dealings with trappers. The Indians always returned gift for gift, which was a matter of sacred honor. Banjo

40

Mike therefore allotted much of his goods, such as tobacco, as "gifts" for the Indians of the Beaver tribe, knowing that in each case he would get gifts twice the value of the stuff he had given. This was also a matter of honor among the Indians.

Banjo Mike had been on his way up the Peace River, making his usual circuit through the wild country of the trappers and Indians—which took him the better part of a year—when he, ran into the gold hunters. Since they were going in his direction, he stayed with them, glad of the chance for a little human companionship that did not involve association with the Hudson's Bay Company traders.

When the party camped on the east bank of the lower bend of the Peace River, a big Irishman called Tiny had dropped his pack and tent roll on the beach, snatched a wooden pan from the pile, and hastened to the edge of the water to start panning for gold.

The first wash brought up several grains of yellow sand, and everyone in camp forgot all about setting up their tents and began furiously to pan the gravel along the beach. Here was gold—the lure that had drawn them across the plains of Saskatchewan and over the mountains! Here was a fortune!

Banjo Mike sat in his tent, chewing methodically on his "knick-kneck"—the Indian version of tobacco, which consisted of some pure tobacco mixed with red willow bark. Mike used "knick-kneck," not by preference, but because tobacco was more valuable for trading than it was for chewing. Now he grinned sardonically at the gold diggers, suddenly beset with "gold fever." Mentally he figured how much they would pan, and unconsciously he added this to his own finances, since he knew that ultimately he would get practically all of it.

The Irishman, Tiny, strode by waving his wooden pan.

"Hey Mike—come on and stake yourself a claim! The river's that full of gold! Ye don't have to sluice the stuff. It jumps right out at ye!"

Banjo Mike grinned and shrugged. Work was distasteful to him, and in this case it would have been ridiculous. He glanced across the shimmering waters of the river, glowing in the dull haze of the cold northern sky, and saw several small movements against the far shore.

"Injuns!" he muttered, narrowing the slits of his sharp blue eyes. "It's them damn Beavers!" He wondered whether they were braves on the warpath, or perhaps just migrating Indians. He also wondered how many skins they might have—if they were on a peaceful voyage. It was an odd time of the year for the Beaver braves to be on the move.

Banjo Mike said nothing about what he saw. He had no intention of revealing his discovery to the others in the miners' camp until he had explored the various possibilities in the situation.

He looked around for Dan Williams. This huge black man had been a source of profound satisfaction to Mike. Dan and Joe were not interested in digging for gold, and when they were not doing chores for Donald Ross, they were available for any roustabout's work around the mining camp.

Banjo Mike contrived, through an understanding of human nature, to occupy most of Dan's spare time. In a way, he acquired a manservant in the wilderness. And in addition to everything else, the huge black man could shoot. No one who had ever seen him drop a moose with his trusty Sharps breechloader at three hundred yards could doubt it.

Now, as he watched the Indian canoes slip quietly under the shadowy willows on the opposite shore, he looked around for Dan, whom he had "lent" to one of the miners, a fellow named Ephraim Jones. He saw the big black man, cupped his hands, and called out in a low, penetrating voice:

"Hey, Dan—come on up!"

Dan looked up and saw Banjo Mike. He dropped a shovel he was sharpening for Ephraim, and lumbered up the beach toward Mike's small shack, his broad shoulders hunched forward in an unconscious effort to bring himself down to other people's size.

"Get your canoe!" Mike called. "We're goin' trading!"

He ducked into his own cabin and sorted over a few items that he kept for Indian trading, mostly small things to be used

42

to find out if the Beavers were in a bargaining mood. Dan went down to the edge of the river, hauled Banjo Mike's canoe down to the water, and tossed the paddles into the hull.

Across the river Attalu, one of the greatest of the Beaver braves, and his followers had drawn their canoes quietly into the shadow of the trees that lined the beach. Only the sharpest eye would have detected the presence of an encampment of perhaps forty people. In the center of the group sat Attalu.

Strange events had taken place in the village of Komaxala, the chief of the Beavers. The Spirit of Evil had entered the heart of Attalu, bringing misfortune upon the whole tribe. Attalu now had established himself as a new chief and wore the full regalia, including the strings of clamshells around his neck.

Attalu's keen eyes saw every movement on the opposite bank. He could see the one whom he knew as a trader rise in front of his wooden tepee and motion to a huge man to join him, and together they climbed into a canoe and set out for the far shore. The big man wielded the paddle, and to all outward appearances the mission seemed peaceful.

When Banjo Mike was close enough to the opposite shore to be heard, he shouted in a loud voice that carried across to the bank:

"Bo yu!" This meant "How do you do!"

These were not the kind of Indians Banjo Mike expected. He motioned to Dan, who crouched in the canoe facing him, to slow down the churning of his paddle. He wanted the canoes to be broadside to the bank so he could observe the Indians without seeming to be curious.

No one lifted a hand. Attalu sat among his braves, staring steadily at the approaching canoe. If he recognized Banjo Mike, he did not show this by so much as a flicker of expression.

Banjo's greeting might have fallen on a tribe of deaf mutes. He was close enough now to make out the headdress and the elaborate gear Attalu wore around his neck. He was sitting among his braves on a ledge above the riverbank.

43

He's been in a fight! Banjo Mike said to himself; and he knew Attalu had got the worst of it!

Banjo Mike knew the character of these Indians. Attalu had decorated himself so that he would look like the most powerful chief in the world. This would dispel any idea that he had suffered a recent reverse. His head was shaved from the side of his head, leaving only a tuft on top and braided locks that fell from the temples. He sat among his braves, silent and regal, gazing proudly and without any display of curiosity at the canoe, which was now pointing toward the bank.

In a few minutes Banjo Mike got out of the canoe and motioned for Dan to pull it up on the bank. He took several articles with him, including some pouches of tobacco. This would be sufficient to initiate the trading. When he found out what had happened that made the Indians act so queerly, he would bring over more items for bartering. The first thing was to have a few gifts for Attalu, and he knew an Indian could always use tobacco, and perhaps a knife.

The Indians were on a flat area, a few feet above the level of the river. The campsite had been carefully selected, with the customary caution of the Indian warrior. In order to reach it from the river, it was necessary to go around a promontory covered with heavy underbrush.

Banjo Mike motioned for Dan to follow; they pushed through the brush and after two or three minutes of climbing, emerged on the upper level. Banjo Mike stared in astonishment at the camp. Only a few braves remained with Attalu, who sat before his tepee—the tallest in the camp. The others had moved away silently into the brush.

Banjo Mike observed Attalu's countenance; then he turned quickly to Dan.

"Go back and get your gun," he said quietly. "These damn Indians look fusty to me. Something's cooking."

Dan turned and headed down through the brush toward the beach. Banjo Mike continued to watch Attalu, and he observed that the Beaver chief was watching Dan. His black eyes fol-

44

lowed the figure of the big black man, but not a word passed his lips.

Peace River runs through the middle of a wide valley, with mountains on both sides ascending toward high plateau country. Forests cover the mountains on all sides, but near the river there are many dense thickets of underbrush, including willows growing close to the riverbank.

Dan disappeared into these willow thickets, on his way back to the canoe to get his gun; meanwhile, Banjo Mike felt it necessary to find out the mood of the Indians. If they wanted to trade, he was ready; if not, he was ready to move.

"How!" he finally said to Attalu. He held up the pouch of tobacco.

Attalu should have nodded gravely; but he continued to stare at the place where Dan had plunged into the thicket.

This is a hell of a note! Banjo Mike thought. These Indians have either gone crazy—or they are ready to shoot us from the bushes!

"Where are your braves?" he asked Attalu.

The chief said nothing, and Banjo Mike's uneasiness increased. The few braves who had remained in camp now moved back toward the farther edge of the small camp area, and almost in a twinkling, they also vanished.

God damn that black son-of-a-bitch! Banjo Mike thought. Why doesn't he come with that gun?

To Attalu he said:

"There is much food in the forest—plenty of game. But a great chief should have a good knife." He brought a hunting knife out of his sack of trading goods and laid it on the ground at Attalu's feet. The chief did not touch it. Instead, he pointed a finger at the place where Dan had entered the thicket.

"He is black!" he said.

So that's it, Banjo Mike thought. His bristling face, covered with many weeks' growth of whiskers, twitched in a momentary grin. The old scoundrel is afraid of Dan—or is he?

"It is a black spirit, old chief," he said. "The black man does

45

my bidding. He is powerful and shoots well. That you must tell your braves."

He looked around suggestively, but Attalu said nothing.

Down near the river, Banjo Mike could hear the crash of Dan's big body, moving into the brush. A maddened moose could not have made more noise. Banjo Mike knew the Indians' contempt for the careless woodcraft of white men, and he hoped he could signal Dan quickly enough when he emerged, to maintain a silent dignity. This would impress the Indians; whereas Dan's customarily cheerful camaraderie would have exactly the opposite effect.

Banjo Mike waited patiently and cautiously, knowing the Indian mentality. The next few seconds would tell the tale— whether Banjo Mike would be able to trade successfully, taking full advantage of the uncertainty created in Attalu's mind by the presence of this strange black giant, or whether he and Dan would be wiped out by an ambush of Beaver braves.

At that moment, from the direction in which Dan was plowing through the underbrush, there came the sound of a shot.

CHAPTER FOUR

The events which had occurred in the Beaver tribe, shortly before Banjo Mike observed Attalu and his warriors drifting down the river, were unknown to anyone outside the tribe. Yet among the Beavers they had created the most serious situation since that time, many generations before, when the Beavers were driven out of the plains to the east by the Chippewas.

The Beavers had carried on many wars with the Chippewas in those days; and finally, when many of their warriors were killed, they had fled westward to the broad lowlands that extend from the Peace River westward to the Rockies. This winding river, flowing down from the snowy slopes of the mountains, toward the Slave River and Lake Athabaska, was so quiet and broad that the Beavers called it *Un-je-gah,* which means Peace. It would have borne that name proudly for many generations if the Spirit of Evil had not entered the hearts of a few men.

The incident which stirred Banjo Mike's curiosity had been a comparatively small one: Attalu had shot an arrow through Komaxala's dog. The shooting of the dog was not in itself an evil thing; but since Komaxala was the chief, a matter of tribal honor was involved.

It was never quite known whether Attalu shot the dog by accident or design. The braves were hunting when it happened, and Attalu—who hardly wanted it believed that any act of his was accidental—brought the dead dog back and threw it at Komaxala's feet, shouting: *"How! Oma ka pa me je ten!"* which means "Look what I have thrown at you!"

47

Komaxala looked at the dog, with the arrow sticking from its side. No one seemed angered by what had happened. The warriors squatted around a fire, the older ones sitting on the lee side where the smoke drove away the mosquitoes. It was assumed that an evil spirit had somehow gotten into Attalu and directed the arrow.

Komaxala, a tall powerful man with a face like a Roman, finally turned to Attalu and shouted, *"Tapwa kitut tumi hin!"* which, loosely translated, meant "What a fine thing you have done for me!" With that, he seized a heavy stick that had been lying at his side and aimed a swinging blow at Attalu's head.

Attalu, who had been on the alert for just such a thing as this, ducked his head and jumped to his feet. Everybody seemed to join on one side or the other, and before the fire had died down for lack of attention, sixty Beaver braves had been felled, many of them fatally, without profit to anyone, since Komaxala's dog was already dead.

The warriors sat down again to a council. There were a few gaps in the ranks but those who were fit for the deliberations decided that the ancient law of the tribe must be enforced: Attalu and his family and relatives, and those who fought on his side against the chief, must leave the Peace River and find themselves a home elsewhere. None could ever return without loss of honor, nor could their children return. Only the third generation might come back to the Peace River and join the tribe of their fathers.

There was no further violence. Attalu and his followers set out in their canoes before the sun had risen. Proudly they moved out on the broad surface of the Peace River and turned downstream, toward the bend below Dunvegan. As the trees slid slowly past along the riverbank, Attalu's keen eyes took in every detail, reading the secret messages of the forest. His ears, as sharp as those of a bobcat, detected every familiar noise as well as unfamiliar noises. One of these unfamiliar noises was the sound of loud voices and the rattle of strange weapons. Beyond the great bend of the river, on a wide sand beach on the side toward the rising sun, he saw many tents.

Smoke rose from many fires, which had been built with wood that burned swiftly and gave off much smoke.

It was always a mystery to the Indians that white men could violate so many natural laws, such as building a fire with wood that smoked, and still remain alive. Their tents were built in the most exposed places, with no thought of concealment. It was as if they obstinately refused to take precautions that were normal to all people.

For this reason the Indians stayed away from white men, not wanting to be infected with their lack of culture. Even when they went on the warpath against white people, it was with a fatalistic foreboding that the Indians themselves in the long run would suffer defeat. All this gave rise to a feeling that the spirits protected white men, even when they were stupid—as they usually were.

Banjo Mike was aware of this. He knew that Attalu would not hesitate to kill him if he felt he could do it and escape; but Attalu, like all Beavers, would not risk the retaliation of the Spirits. And it was for this purpose that Mike sought to introduce his black handyman as a new and powerful "black spirit."

He had already decided, as he sat facing Attalu in his warrior chief's ornaments, that there were too many suspicious circumstances to make it wise for him to remain and attempt to trade. He was on the point of making a decision to get out, and was only waiting for Dan to return with his gun.

Now, when he heard the sound of shots in the brush, Mike reached his decision instantly and without subtlety. He jumped up and ran for the beach. The first shot was followed by four or five more in rapid succession.

Mike was convinced that Dan had been ambushed; and since it served no purpose for him to remain and be shot at, he headed directly over the embankment, plunging down the steep slope to the beach where the canoe had been dragged partly out of the water.

Without pausing in his speed he leaped for the canoe, grabbing up a paddle as he sprawled in the bottom of the craft. The impact jarred the canoe loose from the beach, and in a matter of seconds Mike was paddling lustily for the far shore.

Back in the brush, Dan turned and watched this strange performance. All he knew was that he had shot a moose. The moose and her calf had come running across the projection of land which Dan had to cross in order to reach the upper level where the Indians were camped. Close behind were a scattering of wolves—perhaps four or five. Dan did not count them. He had one bullet in his gun, and he fired, dropping the lead wolf in its tracks.

Then mechanically he reached in his pocket and extracted bullets, regularly slipping them into the breach, raising his rifle and firing. Each complete maneuver required only a few seconds. In less than a half minute, the last of the wolves, which had leaped forward and fastened its teeth in the leg of the calf, lay squirming on the ground in its death agony.

The moose had turned when the huge black wolf had leaped at the calf. These black wolves are different from those that roam the plains. They seldom howl, but are given to growling, like an angry bear. And in times of hunger they ravage the forested country, attacking animals of any size. The moose is normally more than a match for a black wolf; it can turn its great scythelike horns and rip the belly of a wolf from neck to tail. But the moose in this case had to protect her calf, which would not have been able to cope with the wolf; therefore she had turned to run.

When the last wolf jumped the calf, however, the moose cow turned and stood over her young, swinging her giant head defiantly. Here nose was pointed high, as if she would determine the source of the next attack by scent alone. At that instant, Dan, having mechanically shoved another shell in the firing chamber of his Sharps, fired at the moose, and she tumbled over. The calf, still bawling in pain, scampered into the woods, the only survivor of the brief battle.

Dan laid down his rifle and walked over to look at the moose. It was a big one—enough to fill the whole camp on steaks for several days. He grinned, and turned toward the Indian camp, intending to resume his approach through the brush. At that moment he saw Banjo Mike running headlong toward the beach.

For several seconds Dan stood bewildered. Mike jumped into the canoe with such force that he might have run his foot through the bottom. In less than a minute he was out in the river, paddling furiously for the shore where the miners were camped.

Dan shook his head. He thought of calling out, but Banjo Mike was already halfway across the river. He was moving fast now, with long, deep strokes that made the water boil behind the canoe.

Dan started toward the Beaver camp. When he arrived there, he was surprised to find no one around.

Dan's only knowledge of Indians was from those who came into the trading posts. He had never seen an Indian in his native habitat. Those he had seen were not good-looking, and they seemed to move around like shadows in the trading posts, seldom speaking, and then only in grunts.

Now he stared around at the camp. Signs of the Indians were there: the fires, still smoldering slightly, and the large pointed tent of Attalu, rising above the others. But the chief and his warriors had disappeared, along with Banjo Mike.

Dan seldom occupied himself with speculation. He had just killed a big moose cow, and his thoughts immediately returned to the animal. It should be good eating; and it had been some days since the men in the camp had eaten anything but rabbits and a few small deer that had come out early after the thaw, gaunt and half-starved from the long winter's fast.

It did not occur to Dan that Banjo Mike might not return. He knew the Lord Jesus was always there to guide him and tell him what to do; and when Banjo Mike was around, Dan assumed that he spoke with the authority of the Lord Jesus. Now that Banjo had gone off in a hurry, Dan supposed it was on some mission of his own—perhaps to get more tobacco to trade with the Indians; or he might have gone to the miners' camp to tell them about the big moose Dan had shot.

Dan suddenly remembered that he had left his gun lying on the ground when he went to look at the moose. He turned and ran toward the place in the woods where the moose lay, muttering aloud, "Oh, Lord Jesus, for the sake of yo' wounds, don't let them damn Indians get Dan's gun!"

The prayer seemed to be effective because the gun was lying there when he reached the spot. Dan stopped a minute, to bow this head in thanks and then decided he had better cut up the moose before the meat got bad. The animal was too big to carry down to the beach, where Banjo Mike would be able to see it when he returned in his canoe. Dan then set about quartering the animal, using his knife to cut the tendons and separate the huge shoulder and hip joints. Dan was a cook, and he knew which steaks would be the tenderest. It was not long before he was completely absorbed in the job of butchering the moose, singing snatches of songs out of the joy of singing, and completely disregarding any notion that Indians might be lurking around.

Banjo Mike meanwhile had reached the opposite shore. He turned to look back, after he had drawn his canoe up on the bank, and was startled to see the smoke of a fire issuing from the trees across the river.

Them damn varmin's burning poor old Dan! he thought.

Banjo Mike returned to his shack, tossed the bag of trading goods inside. Then he squatted on the single wooden step at the entrance, gazing dispiritedly across the river. If Dan had survived the ambush, he was doubtless even now suffering a worse fate than death. He watched the miners, hurrying senselessly from their shacks to the river and back to their shacks again, always in the strange pursuit of gold. Some of the, miners had worked out a better method of panning: they built large wooden boxes, with fine screens on the bottom, which they used to sluice the gravel in much larger quantities. For this purpose they needed picks and shovels; and these were items which Banjo Mike carried in stock, often trading them for sums equal to all the gold that one man could dig in a week of hard work.

While Banjo Mike sat pondering on these matters, Ephraim Jones came by and stopped to peer through the gloom at Banjo Mike.

"Hello—Banjo?" Banjo Mike grunted affirmatively.

"Got a pick and a shovel?" the man asked. "I got a big rocker, and I need more dirt for it. My old spade is worn down to the handle."

"Can't say right off, Eph," Banjo Mike said. "I got my own tools, but I need 'em."

Ephraim approached the shack.

"That's what Dan Ross told me. What in hell do you need 'em for—you ain't diggin'! You damn traders is all alike! All right —what do you want for it?"

Banjo Mike rose leisurely. Across the river, against the darkening sky he could see the faint trace of smoke against the dying daylight in the west. He looked at Ephraim a moment, and then said:

"Maybe I could let you have 'em, Eph—but I got a job to do."

"I'll pay whatever you ask, you damn pirate. I got to have the tools!"

Banjo Mike nodded, and looked across the river.

"Nigger Dan is across there," he said. "I got to get over an' help him out, Eph. If you was to help me—maybe I could give up a mite on them tools you ast for."

Ephraim came closer. His heavy face, bristling with graying whiskers that stood out like thistle stalks on a burned field, showed a sudden gleam of avid curiosity.

"You say Dan's across the river?" he asked, his neck swelling slightly, contracting the muscles of his throat so that his voice seemed to choke. "By God, Mike, if you hit something——"

Banjo Mike shook his head emphatically.

"I ain't hit nothin', Eph! It's Dan. It's like I said, he's across the river——"

"Get the damn tools an' come on!" Eph said hoarsely. "I'll pay you anything you ast—only get goin'!"

Banjo Mike went into the shack and came out with a shovel and pick. He handed one to Ephraim and took the other under his arm. They started together down to the beach where Banjo Mike had left his canoe.

They passed two miners, hurrying back to their diggings in order to be able to work a few more pans of gravel before night set in. One of the men saw the shaft of the shovel under Ephraim's arm.

"Where you goin' with that spade?" he asked.

Ephraim said nothing; but Banjo Mike turned to the man and said, "Eph is goin' across the river with me to help Nigger Dan." They continued quickly down to the beach. One of the miners ran after them.

"What in hell's Nigger Dan doin' across the river?" he asked, and tried to grab the handle of the shovel Ephraim was carrying. "Let me use your spade while you're gone, Eph. There ain't a damn spade that's any good in camp."

Eph tugged the handle free and started running for the canoe. Banjo Mike was a few steps behind, and he looked back and saw a dozen miners gathering with the two that had accosted them.

In a few minutes Banjo Mike and Eph were in their canoes, out in the river and paddling rapidly. Behind them men had gathered on the shore. A few called to them, and several canoes were pushed into the water. By the time Banjo Mike's canoe was halfway across the Peace River, a flotilla of small craft was following.

Ephraim paddled grimly, while Banjo Mike sat in the stern steering and paddling his canoe, effortlessly but swiftly. Once the big miner turned to shout across at Banjo Mike: "Why in hell did you shoot off your God-damn mouth, Banjo? Them other fellows would never know'd you struck anything——"

"I didn't say I struck anything," Banjo Mike replied; but he doubted that Ephraim heard him.

Dan saw the approaching flotilla, and wondered if Banjo

Mike had told the whole camp about the moose. If so, he had ample steaks for all. He grinned at the notion of the hungry miners paddling across the river for the juicy moose meat which already was broiling on the fire. He counted a dozen boats, and went back and tossed twice that many slabs of meat across the green saplings he had placed as a grill over the fire.

Several of the canoes had almost caught up with Ephraim and Banjo Mike when they reached the shore. They piled out, the other miners scarcely bothering to drag their canoes far enough up the beach to avoid having them washed into the river. The bright beacon of Dan's fire shone through the dusk, and the miners rushed up from the riverbank.

Banjo Mike had already seen the fire on the beach and the single figure moving around it. He knew that whatever had happened to the Indians, nothing had happened to Dan!

Cursing under his breath, Banjo Mike began to figure out what to do. A score of miners had joined the hegira across the river, presumably to share in the strike which they thought Banjo Mike and Dan had made.

Banjo Mike was not inexperienced in the matter of mining camp temperament. He considered all the possibilities carefully, as he hauled his canoe ashore and took time to tie the painter to a large rock. Then he followed the other miners up to Nigger Dan's fire.

"How far upland did you go, Dan?" one asked. "Let's see how much color you got?"

Banjo Mike stood in the rear. He still had not figured out what to do when the miners discovered there was no gold. Meanwhile, Dan had passed out some of the meat, but none of the miners took any. Banjo Mike was hungry, and when the others had rushed on toward the woods to cut green stakes to mark their claims, he went over to the fire and took a big piece of meat Dan handed him.

The sound of voices rang up and down the beach, and Banjo Mike decided that if the Indians really wanted to stage a massacre, this was the time. He looked at Dan. The big

55

Negro was grinning with delight because he was providing meat for everyone.

The miners were already wrangling over their claims on the beach. A few had finished staking and were out at the edge of the water, panning under the vague light of Nigger Dan's fire. Others had unrolled blankets and were preparing to sleep. These were the seasoned men who knew how to make each move count. Others hung around the fire where Dan was broiling steaks, belaboring the Negro with questions.

"How in hell did you find the stuff?" one miner asked. He was a burly man, with reddish whiskers and a scar like a white line across his throat. He was known as Left-handed Jim because he used his right hand for everything but shooting. "You and Banjo ain't miners. How in hell did you find it?"

Dan's big teeth flashed in the light of the fire.

"Some wolves were after it, Massa Lef' Hand. I done shot them wolves, an' then I shot the moose. I jes' shot once at the moose. Like I tol' yo' all, Dan don' never shoot but once."

Left-handed Jim regarded Dan suspiciously, and finally shook his head and walked away. He and his partner had staked a claim directly below Dan's fire, and it would be necessary to fend off any nocturnal claimants to the area.

One by one the miners came back toward the fire. Those that had staked claims and were ready for the night were ready to eat. Banjo Mike had moved up to the fire and now squatted near it, chewing on the steak Dan had pulled out for him. He had not spoken to Dan since he arrived. Now he sat staring moodily at the fire.

There were a score of steaks lying in the sand, tossed there by the miners who were far more interested in gold than in moose meat. Dan meanwhile was broiling new steaks for anyone that arrived.

Banjo Mike knew that the mood of the miners would quickly become mean once they discovered there was no gold. There had been some gold found at the camp near old Fort St. John, after Tiny's first strike. But not much. Everyone in the camp suspected that others had struck pay dirt, and had concealed their good luck; but no one was willing to admit his own failure. The sudden rush for the diggings across the river was like a release from pent-up disappointment. Each miner figured this was the chance to retrieve his bad fortune; however when Banjo Mike's ruse was exposed, he knew disappointment would change to ungoverned rage.

Dan had heard enough talk of gold by this time to know that the miners had come across the river to dig for gold. He asked Banjo Mike:

"Where-at is this gold, Massa Mike? Ev'body say we got gold. All I got is moose meat."

Banjo Mike nodded.

"I never told any of 'em there was gold, Dan. But them damn miners thinks gold—they got nothin' else to think about! So when I came back to help you——"

Banjo Mike waved his hand in a gesture of futility. He had been thinking ever since he pulled his boat ashore. Now he was at the end of it. There was nothing to do but wait.

Dan looked at Banjo Mike for a while, but he still understood little of what was going on. However, he knew men had to eat so he kept on broiling moose steaks.

CHAPTER FIVE

Banjo Mike woke up just as the dawn began to color the sky across the river to the east. He could see the metallic gleam of water against the lightening horizon and a few scattered fires on the beach. Shadowy figures moved back and forth like fretful ghosts. The smoke touched the cool air with acrid fumes.

On a shelf of land above the edge of the river was the smoldering glow of Dan's fire. Banjo Mike could see Dan's huge bulk, crouched in a sitting position near the fire. He was apparently asleep in this position, because Banjo Mike watched for some time, and Dan did not move.

Down on the beach he could see some of the miners, industriously whittling at green branches which they were shaping for stakes to replace the ones they had hastily driven into the sand the night before to mark their "claims."

Banjo Mike's mouth twisted into a grin. He knew the feeling of the gold diggers: they would continue to believe there was gold on the beach simply because it was always regarded as foolish to be the first to admit failure. Any miner who expressed lack of faith in gold deposits, no matter where he was digging, automatically reduced the value of his own claim. Banjo Mike figured it would take about six hours before the miners would begin to talk to each other about the lack of "color." When disillusionment set in, it would be fast.

Banjo Mike thought about pulling out quietly, before daylight. But this would mean he would have to arouse Dan and quietly make him understand what had happened—which was impossible; or else he would have to abandon the black man to his fate again.

Ephraim came over and stood for a moment, waiting for Banjo Mike to say something. Mike was silent. Finally Ephraim broke the silence. He swore, by God, that he had found "color" in some gravel he dug from the roots of the long grass on the ledge above the river.

"I dug the gravel under the spruce needles," he said, looking hopefully at the old trader. "I got my sticks down there. Want to see it?"

Banjo Mike shook his head. "If you got some gold, that's a hell of a lot more than I got," he said.

"What do you mean? You said you'd found color—and we can't even find out where in hell you staked your claim!"

Banjo Mike looked at his friend with tired eyes.

"I ain't staked my claim, Eph," he said. "I told you I had to come across the river to help Dan. I thought the Injuns had him——"

Ephraim looked at the trader, his round face suddenly frozen with understanding.

"You got all them damn miners to come over here——?"

Banjo Mike nodded again.

Ephraim turned and walked down the beach. Two young miners were standing nearby, debating on the value of their claims. They had been panning most of the night, and there wasn't a show of color. They were younger and newer than the rest, and they were quite ready to confess they had found nothing.

Ephraim stalked past the pair, and their heads swiveled as they turned to follow him. One of the men overtook Ephraim, and Banjo Mike watched the pantomime. He was unable to hear what was being said, but he knew what the outcome would be. Ephraim would tell them, with some bitterness, what Banjo Mike had said. In a short time the entire camp would know that neither Banjo Mike nor Nigger Dan had ever staked a claim on Peace River.

With fatalistic eyes Banjo Mike watched the scattering of miners as they moved in small groups along the river edge. He was even able to grin under the thick bristle of red hair. He knew what was happening, and most galling of all would be the arrival of the other miners from across the river, curious to see what was going on. Then the score of men who had chased Mike and Ephraim across the river would have to take the ribbing of those who had stayed back at Fort St. John—and Banjo Mike knew that spelled trouble.

Already a suspicion had been developing that the diggings at Fort St. John were quite literally a flash in the pan. Few of the miners were ready to confess this openly, but Banjo Mike knew that very little color had been found in the gravel since Tiny had panned the first sign of gold.

Dan meanwhile had aroused himself, and stirred up the fire. He tossed a few more steaks on the embers and the miners drifted up to the fire, attracted by the aroma of burning meat. When Dan had handed out all the moose meat steaks they would eat, he carried the rest of the fresh meat down to Banjo Mike's canoe. He knew Donald Ross, the trader, would be happy to have fresh meat. Dan and Joe still considered themselves workers for the Hudson's Bay Company factor, although their services were available to anyone, usually without charge.

Banjo Mike followed the big Negro down to the edge of the river and climbed into the canoe.

"Let's get the hell out of here," he said. After they pushed off, the other miners followed, since there was no longer any particular reason to remain on the beach.

Dan carried the meat up to the trading post and told Donald Ross what had happened. Dan was not quite sure just what had brought so many miners across the river; so he said nothing about that. He told Ross that he had killed a moose, and the Indians, instead of trading with Banjo Mike, had run away. And then Mike and all the miners had come paddling across the river.

Joe Potter heard the miners talking about the gold strike, and he asked:

"Where-at is this gold you an' Massa Mike found?"

Donald Ross listened carefully. This was all quite important. He had planned to enlarge the post for the Hudson's Bay

Company, but if the prospectors remained in the area, he knew it would be useless to expect the Indians to come to the post to trade.

"I don't know nothin' about gol'," Dan said. "All these folks put sticks in the groun' an' claim they got lots of gol'. But Dan don't see no gol'."

Donald Ross decided he had better see Banjo Mike and find out what actually happened. Mike told him the whole story. Ross was an old hand in the trading game, and he knew a little about gold diggers. He asked Mike:

"Who is going to be blamed for this? Dan is an employee of the Company, and I am responsible for him. Maybe you'd better talk to the miners."

Banjo Mike looked at the trader. His eyes were blue and at times they were as cold as the water of a mountain lake.

"If you an' the Company want to be responsible for Dan," he said slowly, "you go an' talk to the miners. If you want me to handle it, I'll tell Dan to get the hell out of camp—an' I'll foller him!"

Ross shook his head. He was a thin, serious Scotsman, with streaks of candor and stubbornness. He had been in the service of the Hudson's Bay Company for nearly thirty years, and it was inconceivable to him that a group of miners could harass the Company. In this case Dan Williams was part of the Company, and to abandon him would be like abandoning Company property.

He had no opportunity to reply to Banjo Mike, however. There was a noise outside the door of Banjo Mike's shack, and Mike threw open the door. Three men were standing in front of the shack. He saw Ephraim, who had unwittingly led the rush across the river; and behind him was Left-handed Jim. The third was a miner named Bob.

"Where's that damned nigger?" Left-handed Jim asked. Ross stood in the doorway with Banjo Mike, but said nothing. Mike finally said:

"He's inside. What do you want to see him about?"

Dan had pushed his way into the doorway, and the three

61

men saw him. Left-handed Jim waved his hand, and shouted:

"Tell that black son-of-a-bitch to come out here and tell us where that gold is—or we'll drag him out!"

He stepped forward as Dan came through the door. The Negro was so large that he blocked the other two from the view of the three miners. Standing on the steps, he towered over everyone, his white teeth shining in an apologetic smile. When he spoke his voice was soft and deep.

"Dan don't lie to anyone," he said. "Nobody ever said Dan foun' gol'."

The admission was too much for Left-handed Jim. He swung at Dan, hitting the big Negro squarely on the jaw. Dan sat down, rubbing his chin and staring at the miners.

Mike and Donald Ross came through the door. Mike had a shovel in his hand as he jumped off the step, and he hit Left-handed Jim in the chest so hard the tall miner staggered back a dozen steps and sat down on the ground. Ephraim, who had suffered perhaps the most of anyone, grabbed Banjo Mike's shoulder and swung him around.

"Who ast you to shove your damn nose into this?" he growled, and swung a blow at Mike, which Mike easily ducked.

Donald Ross remained on the top step, shouting to the men to stop brawling; but Joe Potter, who was used to fighting, jumped off the step and landed on Ephraim's back. With this extra burden, and Joe's black arms wrapped around his neck and face, Ephraim was unable to defend himself, and Banjo Mike, who had dropped the shovel and was now using his fists, knocked him backward on top of Joe.

Donald Ross went out and helped Dan to his feet. Meanwhile a number of miners had collected in front of Mike's shack. Few of the men cared to tackle Mike—not merely because he had a reputation as a tough man to put away in a fight, but he was known to all the Indians, and his enemies feared to travel in the woods where Indians might want to avenge an attack upon their friend.

Donald Ross had drawn his revolver, which he always carried, not so much as a weapon as a symbol of authority. He stood now, with the gun in his hand, and no one was quite sure what he intended to do with it.

"Get back, ye ragamuffins!" he said in a fierce voice. His hand trembled, not with fear and uncertainty but with anger. "Th' mon that lays a hand on yon black boy wi' get a bullet a-tween the ees—an' don't be guessin' aboot it!"

The miners drew back. Most of them were glad of this interruption, which spared them from deciding whether to tackle Banjo Mike and his hard-knuckled fists. Dan was standing again, a towering figure among them; and in spite of the blow which felled him, his enormous face seemed calm, except for his eyes which rolled from one side to another.

Banjo Mike and Donald Ross led Dan over to the tent where he and Joe Potter lived, and Donald Ross helped him to wash a cut on his jaw and put liniment on his face and hands. While these medications were being applied a shot rang out and a bullet ripped a hole in the tent, knocking down a lamp which hung from the main pole.

Everyone dropped to the floor. Dan, in falling, managed to reach for his rifle which was propped against the side of the tent. It had become dark outside, and it was evident from the sound of voices that a number of miners had collected near the tent. One of them shouted, "Tell that damned nigger to come out—or we'll blow the tent apart!"

Dan lifted a flap and shoved the barrel of his gun through the opening. He saw several men, and one raised himself, as if he were about to fire a gun. Dan sighted his rifle and shot. The man screamed and fell forward. He kicked aimlessly for a few seconds, and then lay quiet.

Dan saw another figure move in the darkness, and he shoved a cartridge in the gun and fired again. The second figure went down. Dan was about to shoot again, but the other miners turned and ran, and all he could hear was the pounding of their feet in the darkness.

Donald Ross and Banjo Mike came out of the tent. The factor looked at the two dead men, and shook his head. Then he turned to Dan.

"It's best that ye leave now, lad," he said. "They won't be forgettin' this in the mornin'."

Banjo Mike agreed. The miners had shot first, and Dan's shooting had been merely to defend himself; yet he was black, and Mike knew that the miners' mood would rise to a pitch of anger that would be beyond the control of anyone.

Dan said nothing. He permitted Banjo Mike to throw a few things into a bag, and Ross went to his store and brought back ammunition for Dan's gun and tobacco to trade with the Indians. Dan brought out his Bible, which he had always carried with him on his travels. Donald Ross glanced at the Bible, his sharp eyes twinkling.

"Ye'd do well to remember your prayers, and save the space for somethin' for your belly—but God bless ye anyway, lad!"

They were ready to make their way in the darkness down to the boat, but Dan suddenly knelt down and clasped his hands in front of his face, bowing his huge head.

"Sweet Jesus!" he said, in a loud voice. "Dan is goin' to need Yo' mighty bad right now!" He stopped a moment, and then as an afterthought said: "Dan don' do nothin' mean to nobody, Lord Jesus—jes' remember that!"

Banjo Mike went out of the tent to see if any miners were lurking around. Then the other three followed him down to the edge of the river. Joe carried most of the goods Dan was taking with him, and he piled these in Dan's canoe.

Dan carried his gun and his Bible; and while he was stowing his gun and Bible in the canoe, he saw the figure of a man coming toward the boat. Banjo Mike and Donald Ross had gone back to the camp, and Joe had taken off for the woods when the trouble started; so he was sure it was not one of these.

The figure stopped, and a husky voice suddenly roared out: "Hey, come a-runnin'! The damn nigger is gettin' away!"

The man had a gun, and Dan saw the flash of the shot and heard the sharp zing of a bullet.

"Stop, ye damned black murderer, or I'll drill ye—an' there won't be no need of a miners' court to hang ye!"

64

There were other shouts from the camp, a few feet above the beach, and Dan heard the sound of heavy boots. He could hear Banjo Mike's voice shouting above the rest, telling the men not to shoot.

Dan had tugged his gun from under the pile in the canoe. He swung the gun by instinct, sighted it and shot almost at the same instant. The man dropped across the end of a canoe and hung there, like a half-empty sack.

Dan threw his gun into his canoe, and then shoved several other canoes near his into the water. He knew the river current would quickly take them downstream. He kicked holes in those he could not easily push into the river, so they would not float.

By this time a dozen men were running toward the beach. One man came out of the darkness, charging at Dan, but Dan caught him around the waist and hurled him into the river.

Dan jumped into his canoe, kicking it away from the bank, and reached for his paddle, which always lay against the bow. In a few strokes he was far enough from shore so that the lights from the campfires would not reach him. He lifted the paddle from the water and let the current carry the canoe downstream.

The miners had reached the beach and stood on the bank, cursing bitterly. One man lifted his gun and fired into the darkness. Dan knew he was safe for the moment, until someone could find another canoe, and he roared across the river:

"The Lord Jesus forgive yo'—Dan ain't never comin' back!"

He was silent a moment, and then his laugh, deep and melodious, rolled over the water. One of the miners fired, and Dan could hear the sound of the bullet slapping the water. He had stowed his gun in the canoe, and he was not sure where it was. The shooting frightened him, and he raised the Bible which he had clutched in his hand when he laid down the paddle.

An instant later he heard the sound of a shot and the Bible was wrenched violently from his hands. He was staggered by

E 65

the blow and fell backward, lying full length in the canoe. For several seconds he lay there, half-stunned.

Then Dan gave a wild cry, and reached for the book. It was shattered, but he slipped it under his shirt and crouched in the boat, waiting for the next shot to speed him to his doom. A few more shots were fired, but by this time he was too far out in the stream to be seen.

Dan knew from the shouts that some of the miners were running for their canoes. The lights on the beach showed him the outline of figures ashore, but behind him the velvet cover of darkness had swallowed him completely into the night.

He crouched quietly in the boat for several minutes. Then he took the paddle and softly dipped it into the water. With long, quiet strokes he sent the canoe deeper into the blackness, until he was certain from the dwindling sound of noises on the beach that he was safely out in the river.

Then Dan put the paddle in the bottom of the canoe and stretched out. With the shattered Bible on his chest, he closed his eyes and in a short time was asleep.

CHAPTER SIX

The currents of a river often are more fickle and perverse than the humans who paddle across its surface; and so it was that when the first streaks of dawn lighted the eastern sky, the Peace River, instead of carrying Dan Williams down along its broad course, had shifted the canoe with its sleeping cargo across the river and deposited it upon the far shore, at a point not far from the place where Attalu and his braves had camped—and where the miners of Fort St. John had driven claim-stakes optimistically into the gravel beach. If the miners had been sharp-eyed the next morning they would have observed the lone canoe, motionless against the silent willow trees.

But Dan slept soundly and unobserved until the sun had risen above the tops of the trees that fringed the eastern shore. He finally awakened, and stretched, but it was some time before he could orient himself to his new situation.

He looked across the river, blinking into the sunlight, and tried to understand why he was in his canoe on the far shore. Then he opened his eyes wide, and rolled them as he always did when he was excited. He looked around, gradually recalling the events of the night before.

He suddenly realized that he had drifted ashore—instead of floating downriver!

"Them damn miners!" he exclaimed aloud, and looked across the river. A quick fear rose in his clouded mind. He was no longer safe! He had lost his chance to hide during the night, and in no time the miners would be after him!

Suddenly he remembered that he should have pulled the canoe out of sight. This was what any smart man who was hunted would do. The realization that he had not even thought about this brought a strange fear into Dan's mind. Perhaps there were other things he should do that he had not thought about! If Banjo Mike had been along, he would have known exactly what to do, and would have told Dan. But now there was no one to explain to Dan what he must do. He was alone.

Bein' free ain't easy, Dan thought. He wondered if he should get in his canoe and go back to the camp, and let Banjo Mike and Mr. Ross decide what he should do. Then he remembered what they had told him last night; he must run away, or the miners would kill him! They would hold a miners' meeting, and there was no doubt in Dan's mind what the miners' meeting would decide. He wondered whether, if they caught him, they would shoot him or hang him to a tree.

Dan hoped they would shoot him instead of hang him. He had seen a man hanged once back home in Georgia. He and some other small boys had hidden where they could see it happen, and he had never forgotten the man's face; his eyes were wide open, and his head was pulled so far to one side that it seemed to come out of one shoulder. Dan did not want to die that way. He had seen animals die when they were shot, and this seemed to be the right way to die.

"Dear Jesus!" he muttered aloud. "Don' let the white folks hang Dan!"

Dan knew he should pull the canoe out of sight quickly; but he was also aware that he must keep on the right side of the Lord, so he got down on his knees beside the canoe and prayed. After that he felt better, and he picked up his Bible which lay in the canoe where it had fallen off his chest during the night.

The bullet had gone halfway through the pages, and the back part of the Bible was stuck together. But where the pages opened, he could read some words where the bullet had gone through the paper. It was the forty-first verse of the fifth chapter of Mark; and it read, *"Talitha cumi! . . . Damsel, . . . arise."*

Dan could not understand the Latin words; but the bullet

68

had gone through the phrase "Damsel, . . . arise!" And all that was left was "Dam . . . rise!"

Dan carefully spelled out the word: "D-a-m—r-i-s-e!"

That means "Dan rise," he decided. The Lord was telling him to "get up and go"—even if he had mispelled Dan's name. This was understandable to Dan. The Reverend Sam had often said back in Georgia that all folks were God's children—the black folks as well as the white folks. It was obviously impossible for the Lord to remember the spelling of every name. Dan was so delighted at the message that he quickly forgave the Lord for this slight misunderstanding.

"Dan rise!" he muttered aloud. "That means 'Dan—get up and get on yo' feet!'"

He jumped up and hauled the canoe across the sandy beach and into a clump of willows. He decided to leave it here where he could find it when he came back. He counted the willow trees—there were three; and behind them was a large boulder, half buried. This would make a good marker, Dan decided; and he carefully dragged the canoe into a depression. Then he took out the things he would need—his gun and knapsack, and a hatchet and knife and needles and thread. Banjo Mike had told him the things the Indians liked to get in trading, such as tobacco; but Dan had no idea that he might want to trade, so he left these packages in the canoe. Then he covered the canoe with branches of spruce trees, piling spruce needles on top.

Dan filled his pockets with enough shells for his Sharps breechloader to last for many weeks, and with the bundle strapped on his back, he started through the smaller trees along the river. He stopped once to look across the river at the place where the miners were, but there was no sign of a canoe paddling out toward him. Dan grinned at the way he was fooling them; no one could find the canoe buried under the spruce needles unless he stepped on it. They would never know what happened to Dan!

The thing he put closest to him was the Bible. He shoved this under his heavy woolen shirt, where it would always be with him. With the Bible, and frequent prayers to the Lord and to Jesus, he felt he would be properly ensured against any misfortune.

Dan thought a moment about Joe, who did not have a Bible. Joe seldom tried to read it, but Dan had made up for this forgetfulness by reminding Joe frequently of the things the Reverend Sam had told them, and now and then spelling out a few messages from the Bible.

Dan knew that Joe might easily succumb to the temptations which always beset him, and he wished there had been some way to give Joe protection, too; but it was something he could do nothing about now, so he quickly forgot about it.

For several minutes Dan walked up and down the beach, trying to decide which direction to take. This of course exposed him to the view of anyone from the other side of the river who might be looking, but Dan did not think much about that. The miners apparently did not think much about it, either. No one looked across at him. Finally Dan decided he must make up his mind which direction to take, so he started along the low, swampy country to the west.

For perhaps two or three hours Dan continued in this direction, which kept him near the river, yet moving deeper and deeper into the flat lands which rose far ahead into low hills. Behind these were the Rockies. It was early summer, and the mosquitoes were thick among the rotting pools of water that dotted the country.

Dan had often marveled at the way Indians allowed mosquitoes to alight on their faces, scarcely bothering to brush them off. He had thought: The mosquitoes cannot hurt the Indians, because their skin is so tough. This, of course, was not true. Indians were as badly stung as other men—white or black; but they learned to control themselves, since it would have been unthinkable to let anyone know that such a small insect as a mosquito could bother them.

The further Dan got into the swamps along the river, the worse the stings of the mosquitoes became. At times he stopped and rubbed his face until the stings seemed to disappear; but as soon as he started walking again, the heat of his body made them itch even worse.

At times Dan would sit down and try to cover his face, but the mosquitoes could penetrate the smallest opening. He began to think about going back to the river, where the wind kept the air fairly clear of mosquitoes.

"Lord have mercy on this sinner!" he muttered; and finally dropped to his knees in the wet ground and began to pray aloud. The water soaked into his heavy trousers which the Hudson's Bay Company had furnished him. This made him feel cold and uncomfortable. Around him the thick, wet vegetation of the swamp seemed to form a suffocating enclosure, like a thick fence. No matter what direction he took, the fence was always there. When he plunged through one barrier, there was another beyond it.

Late in the day Dan found himself on higher ground, where the mosquitoes were not so thick. He decided he might as well stay there during the night and start again the next day. He had looked back across the land he had traveled each time he came to a fairly clear place, but there was no sign of anyone following.

Many times as a boy Dan had heard the older folks talk in the evenings about slaves that had escaped. They called this "going over"; but they always were brought back, and they received terrible whippings, and sometimes they died from these whippings. The colored folks had always talked in low voices about this, and mostly about the dogs that followed the men who were running away. The dogs always found them; once the dogs started out, the man would sooner or later be brought back, crazy from fear, and then he would be beaten.

"They ain't goin' to beat Dan!" he muttered aloud; and this thought gave him some comfort. Even if they shot him, it would not be as bad as dying from the terrible beatings. Then he remembered that there were no dogs in the miners' camp like the lean, hungry bloodhounds he had seen on the plantation in Georgia. Most of the dogs were bush dogs, with small, round faces and heavy hair around their necks; and Dan did

71

not think these dogs were good trackers. Most of them were sled dogs.

That night he built a fire, and slept on the side where the smoke drifted, because it was better to smell the smoke than to be bitten by mosquitoes. In the morning he started out again as soon as it was light. He had eaten very little, and hunger began to make him feel faint. It kept him from traveling very fast. At first he had been afraid to shoot anything, because he was still near enough to the river that a shot could be heard. But now he was getting so hungry that he decided to shoot any animal as soon as he saw it.

His direction was now due west, and the ground was higher. The soft places in the ground were fewer and the trees taller. From the top of some of the ridges Dan could see mountains to the west. He headed for these rough-looking peaks, where the snow glistened in the sun. After he was far enough from the river to be safe from the miners, he would make a camp and stay there for several days; then he would return to the river and get the rest of his things out of the canoe.

Dan had no definite idea about what he would do after that. Perhaps there would be people farther west who would not know about him and the fact that he had killed three white men. He might even find Joe, and they could go on farther north together. There was bound to be more freedom up north in the Klondike than there had been on the Peace River, with miners chasing him all the time.

It seemed to Dan that with the Lord on his side—and the miners obviously were men who had little acquaintance with the Lord—he would have nothing to fear; therefore he pushed further from his mind any thought of the old fear of being hunted.

"There ain't no dogs," he said aloud. "Tha's what yo' gotta be scared of—them damn dogs!"

There was little woodcraft in his mode of travel. He pushed through the thickets and brush, shoving larger branches out of his way and making tracks that even a miner could follow. A moose moving sideways through the underbrush could not have made more racket. But he kept moving, with his long, shambling strides; and by the afternoon of the second day he was perhaps twenty-five miles west of the river.

A rabbit jumped through the brush ahead of him, and almost without thinking, Dan raised his gun and fired. The ball of white fur went tumbling end over end, and Dan walked over and laughed gleefully as he picked up the limp carcass.

"Yo' is sure gonna taste good to a man that ain't et for two days!" he murmured, looking almost fondly at the rabbit.

It crossed Dan's mind that the shot might have been heard, but he paid little attention to this. He laughed aloud several times and felt convinced that God Himself had given him the notion of shooting the rabbit, and therefore He would also take care of the fact that somebody might hear the shooting.

Dan took the rabbit some distance before stopping to cook it. In order to cook the rabbit, he would have to make a fire; and this would cause smoke, which could be seen from a distance. However, his hunger was stronger than his caution, and he roasted the rabbit and ate it. Then, feeling much better, he started swinging along again.

He found a long, narrow lake lying between two rows of hills, and he walked for a long time along the shore of the lake. The sight of the lake, and the distant peaks beyond, still coated with snow, gave Dan a sense of being protected; and for the first time since he started from the Peace River, he began to walk without fear.

"Sweet Jesus is he'pin' me now," he said aloud, and enjoyed the sound of his own voice.

After walking for some time, he came to a line of cliffs above the lake, and he climbed these so he could look over the country behind him. Far below he saw the Peace River curving like a long snake through the flat woods. It was wonderful, Dan thought, to have gotten up so high, where there was plenty of freedom and no mosquitoes. This probably was a sign from the Lord that He was leading Dan in the right direction.

By nightfall Dan had cleared the end of the lake, and he was tired; he scraped together a pile of dead leaves, rolled his gun in his coat for a pillow, and almost immediately fell asleep.

When he awakened the first light of day was spreading through the trees, and the lake lay like a white sheet against the blackness of the forest. He was stiff, and he quickly realized that it was quite cold. A strong, freezing wind had blown up during the night.

He crouched for a while, hugging his knees and looking at the lake. He was hungry, and uncertain as to what he should do next. Back at Fort St. John there would have been food and a fire; but out in the woods he had nothing but his clothes and rifle. For a moment Dan wondered if the Lord had been right in leading him out into the forest, where there was no food and no one to tell him what to do.

While he was meditating upon the wisdom of the Lord, he saw a shape move across the edge of the beach. It was a full-grown black bear, drinking water.

Dan picked up his rifle and aimed it at the soft spot behind the shoulder, where the fur hung down. This was the best for a side shot; and almost instantly the sound of the rifle rang across the lake. The bear took a couple of steps and stumbled forward. Dan shouted and laughed, as he always did when he shot an animal; then he started down the slope in a shambling dogtrot.

It was early in the summer, and the bear had not put on much fat. Nevertheless, there was plenty of lean flesh and Dan quickly stripped off the skin and cut several big slabs of meat. He made a fire with his tinderbox, and in a short while was squatting in front of the glowing embers, watching a piece of bear meat, suspended on four green sticks, slowly turn brown.

While he was eating the first piece, he had a second steak broiling over the fire; and so on, until he had eaten a half-dozen pieces of meat. By this time his stomach was so full he knew it would be useless to try to walk any farther that day; so he stretched out on the ground and went to sleep.

For several hours Dan lay on the ground sleeping; when he awakened finally he was so startled by his surroundings that he jumped up and looked up and down the lake. The fear came back to him; he wondered if perhaps he had heard something in his sleep.

There was no sound or sign of anyone, however. Dan decided that an animal must have moved somewhere back in the woods, attracted by the smell of the bear meat. He looked over the meat, and realized that there was so much of it left he could not carry it—and yet it would be foolish to leave it here. He was far enough from the river so that no one would see the smoke of his fire from Fort St. John; therefore, without thinking too much about it, Dan prepared to stay until he had eaten all the bear meat.

He cut down small trees and stripped the branches; then he set the poles in the ground so that they crossed at the tips, making the framework of a hut. Then he laid branches across this, forming a crudely thatched shelter.

He cut strips of the bearskin and tied them around his shoes to keep the soles from wearing out. His rifle and coat he put in the shelter and made himself comfortable, sitting with his back against the opening, which was supported by a heavy pole.

It was pleasant, looking across the lake and thinking about Joe Potter and Banjo Mike and Mr. Ross. While he sat thinking, a deer came slowly along the lake front, lifting its feet gracefully. Dan reached for the rifle. The wind blew from the lake, and the deer had not smelled the smoke of his fire. He aimed his rifle, and in an instant there was a dead deer on the beach.

He laid down his gun and stood for a while in front of the shelter before going down to cut up the body of the dead deer. He got down on his knees, and began to pray aloud, "Oh, sweet Jesus, Yo' done foun' heaven on earth! Yo' done sent that deer for Dan to shoot at, an' Dan don' ever miss what he shoots at!" Dan paused to cackle gleefully at this notion. He knew it was well to give all credit to the Lord in prayer, but it would do no harm to remind Him that he—Dan Williams—had done the shooting. Three times he had shot, and he had a rabbit, a bear, and a deer to show for it.

Dan finished the prayer by saying, "My cup of life is runnin' over, amen!" and this reminded him of something that had worried him since he left the canoe buried on the beach across from Fort St. John.

He had forgotten to bring a cup.

Whenever Dan wanted to drink, he had to bend down to the water and drink like an animal. This disturbed Dan; it was less than the least of men should have . . . a cup!

He walked slowly down to the beach where the body of the deer lay, thinking about the cup. He wondered if there had been one in the equipment he and Joe Potter had thrown hastily into the canoe the night he left Fort St. John.

After he had cut up the deer's body, and hung the hind quarters and the sides to a branch of a tree so that the meat would be above the reach of animals who might come by in the night, Dan went over his small store of equipment. He had a hatchet and a knife, and a tinderbox, and a packet of needles and thread; and in the pockets of his coat he had enough bullets to last for many days.

But there was no cup!

Dan shook his head morosely. Even as a boy, as far back as he could remember, he had always had a cup. He had eaten his first food out of a cup. If a man who was not free could have a cup, certainly a free man should have one.

Something strange took place inside Dan. In his prayers he began to remind God and Jesus that they had forgotten to have him bring a cup. He had set out to find freedom, and now he was a free man; even the miners were no longer hunting him. But what was a free man without a cup?

Maybe Banjo Mike would get me a cup if I went back, Dan thought; and after that he no longer made any plans to continue in the direction he had taken. As soon as he had finished eating the bear meat and deer meat, he would retrace his steps and cross the river in his canoe at night, and find Banjo Mike.

In his isolation in the wild loneliness of the forest, Dan forgot everything except the one thing that disturbed his mind: he had no cup!

Dan did not wait until he had eaten all the meat. Most of the bear meat was still hanging from the trees, and only a quarter of the venison had been eaten, when he gathered his small store of belongings together and some pieces of venison, dried in strips. He knew that when he got near Fort St. John, he could not risk shooting an animal, or making a fire. He must have some dried meat to chew on during the last two or three days of his journey back.

Dan knew that he would get a cup—even if he had to steal it! In the deep recesses of his memory, stealing was much the same as killing. A colored man would be hanged as quickly for stealing as for killing. It was worse than a sin; it was an offense that white men did not forgive.

He took his rifle under his arm, and plunged into the thickets, leading down through the mosquito-infested swamplands that drained into the Peace River from the west. He did not know exactly how he was going to do it, but he knew one thing: he was going to get a cup!

CHAPTER SEVEN

Back at Fort St. John there were a lot of things on the miners' minds besides the whereabouts of Nigger Dan. The most important thing was that no one had found any gold to speak of since Tiny's first strike.

The miners talked over the shooting after Dan left, and except for those who were angry because Dan had kicked holes in their canoes, they agreed that Dan had shot to defend himself. If he had returned to Fort St. John three days after the shooting, he would have been greeted as an old friend.

Even Ephraim, who had been the worst victim of the hoax, admitted he had been excited. Now that it was all washed out, Ephraim agreed that Dan could not be blamed for what happened.

Banjo Mike, whose interests as a trader were not dissimilar to those of Donald Ross—except that Banjo Mike would trade with anyone, and Donald Ross was interested chiefly in Indians—put in a word here and there to stir up the dissatisfaction of the miners. There had been reports of gold on the Fraser River, about two hundred miles to the southwest, and on the Quesnel, where gold was found down in the grassroots —possibly alluvial deposits that had washed down from the mountains and lay in the riverbeds, where it could easily be panned out.

Banjo Mike, knowing that miners without gold are no good for trading, added his own exuberant touches to these stories. Before long the men in the camp were talking openly about moving on. Ephraim was the first to break the ice; he understood that a route existed through the lakes and lower mountains by which they could reach the Fraser River country before the freeze set in. Ephraim said he would travel all the way to the Klondike, if necessary, to find gold; but he was damned if he would stay in this place.

Then Tiny, the only miner who had really struck gold on the Peace River, announced he was ready to move on to the Fraser River. This touched off the rest. Left-handed Jim said he had the same idea; there was no gold at Fort St. John, and he would as soon freeze to death in the Rockies as starve to death on the Peace River!

There was scarcely a miner who was not ready to leave. If Dan had returned at that moment, he would have been asked to join them. The spirit of the camp rose to a new pitch of excitement. They were all set to go! No one wanted to stay an hour more than was necessary.

Joe Potter was urged to join the migration, which aroused Donald Ross' ire. In his mind, Joe was part and parcel of the Hudson's Bay Company, just as much as the trading post or the Company boat which brought supplies regularly from Fort Vermilion.

"There ye go!" he said to Joe, his sharp Scotch voice ringing like a chisel biting into the ice. "A wanderin' ne'er-do-well, like that black psalm-singin' heathen ye chased out of camp! Ye'll end up starvin' in the brakes o' the Fraser when ye could be warm an' eatin' well on the Company's food, an' workin' for your keep!"

Banjo Mike, who understood Joe's philosophy better than the Scotch trader, took the black man aside and arranged to meet him in a few days at the first camp the miners would make—which he knew would not be many miles upstream on the Peace River.

"I'll talk with the old siknflint," he said. "You get yer pay in advance, an' wait for me. There's a lot of tradin' to do with the Beavers, as soon as I find out what in hell ails 'em—an' it might be we'll run across Dan."

Banjo Mike, who had many ways of persuading people, pointed out to Donald Ross that if he let Joe go along as a handyman, the miners would leave all the more quickly. So it

79

was decided that Joe would go along as general handyman and cook; and Donald Ross even agreed to give him supplies as wages for his work for the Company. Banjo Mike saw to it that Joe included needles and knives and things of that sort that could be used for trading with the Beavers.

Just as night settled over the quiet Peace River, the evening before the mass departure from camp was to take place, someone saw a canoe far upriver, floating down along the western shore.

"It's Nigger Dan," one of the miners shouted; and since the funeral of the three miners who had been shot had already been held—with Tiny saying the last official rites over the graves—everyone was in a jovial and forgiving mood.

"Hell, let him come along!" Ephraim said. "We'll have two niggers to do the work for us."

It was soon evident, however, that the man in the canoe was not Dan. He was smaller than the big black man. Although the light was fading, the more sharp-eyed on shore soon detected that the man in the canoe was a white man. He paddled across the river to the rocky shore where the mining camp lay at the foot of a row of scarred and barren hills that rose above the pine-clad slopes. The newcomer eased the craft up to the edge of the beach. He was a rather short man, only a few inches over five feet; but his wide shoulders and heavy head gave an impression of great strength.

He looked at the miners, his black eyes roving from face to face with a certain inquisitiveness that suggested both knowledge and power. He undoubtedly was a man to be reckoned with, even in a land of strong men.

Donald Ross had come down from his trading store, and he lifted a hand as the squat voyager stepped ashore.

"How, Jacques!"

The man in the canoe shook hands warmly with Donald Ross. He was Jacques Pardonet, a trader known across the plains and mountains of western Canada. He had come to the Northwest country some twenty years before, and even before that it was known that he had been in San Francisco and had once seen seven men hanged in the market place of that flourishing port, which made him all the more famous.

After seeing that his canoe was safely beached, and with a careful eye to several bundles of beaver and marten skins that were stowed in the prow of the craft, he turned his attention to Donald Ross.

It seemed that he had suffered a serious misfortune. His canoe had capsized, and among the goods irretrievably lost were two axes—the only ones he had. He was helpless without an ax; but he had met some Indians and managed to trade a few things and the promise of future payment for a poor and badly worn hatchet.

Banjo Mike listened with professional interest to this discussion. He knew that Donald Ross would not like to deplete his store of tools which he kept for trading with the Indians. Yet beaver and marten skins were the same, no matter who trapped them. Banjo Mike had a few tools on hand, and he thought he could strike a bargain. But even more, he wanted to find out from Jacques Pardonet if he had traded recently with the Beaver tribe.

Within a short time Jacques was squatting at a fire, chewing on some of the moose meat that still remained from Dan's kill across the river. He understood quickly the reason for the general state of disintegration about the camp; and he shook his head. He had heard of the gold strike on the Fraser, and the new town of Barkersville that had grown up on the junction of the Antler and Bear rivers.

"I have come from these places—many times," he said, in his sparse English. "It is not easy to find them."

He explained that it was many miles across the Rocky Mountain passes. If the miners left immediately, they might possibly reach the waterfalls on the upper river, where they would have to leave their boats and cross the passes afoot. Even if they reached the passes, they would never reach Barkersville before the freeze; and, of course, there were the Indians.

He looked from face to face. The Indians would track them . . . unless, of course, they were led by someone who knew the Indians better than the Indians knew themselves. Such a man as Jacques Pardonet, for example.

It was soon settled; Jacques Pardonet was unanimously elected the leader of the migration of miners across the Rockies into the Fraser River country.

After these things were straightened out, Banjo Mike told the French trader of his encounter with Attalu and the Beaver braves.

"There is bad time among the Beavers," Jacques said. He told Banjo Mike and Donald Ross of the battle between Attalu and Komaxala, and the banishment of Attalu and his followers from the Beaver tribe.

Banjo Mike nodded. This explained the queer conduct of Attalu and his braves when he and Dan had paddled across the river. The Beavers probably did not have many skins to trade. With such hard times, many of the braves would have drifted away in small bands, or gone to the posts to work as helpers or guides for white trappers. The Beavers had made good trades at one time, and were considered wealthy in the economy of Indians; but they had changed their ways and forgotten the art of storing up food against bad times.

Early the next morning the heavy York boats and lighter canoes were loaded and shoved into the water. The miners were ready to embark. With Jacques sitting aft in one of the York boats like a commander of the fleet, the flotilla pushed off from shore and headed upstream around the bend of the Peace River.

Banjo Mike stood with Donald Ross on the shore. The current was not rapid close to the shore, but it was not long before the last of the boats had disappeared around the bend on the first leg of a long journey to the other side of the Rockies.

Banjo Mike and the trader walked slowly up the short hill to the Company post. Donald Ross was glad they had left; yet his face wore a frown.

"I canna help but feel the lads are chasing something they know little aboot," he said in a dour voice.

Banjo Mike shrugged.

"What did you or I know about this place when we came here, Donald?"

"Aye . . . but in Scotland a lad is born with business in his blood. These men have nothing but thirst—for gold and for whisky. We went away from home always swearin' we'd come back to the old mountains and the poor land—but we never do, o' course. I don't spend a day, Mike, that I don't think o' Scotland. I had meager food, lad, but it was good food and the kind I liked. Even if I ne'er go home, I'll always be thinking o' the old days in Glasgow. But what are these fellows thinking aboot, Mike? Gold and whisky. . . ."

Banjo Mike nodded. He seldom thought about his home, which was in a small Middle Western town in the United States. He had left home when he was a boy, and had no idea how many of his family were still alive.

"How aboot your folks, Mike?" the trader asked, as if he divined Banjo Mike's thoughts, looking at the red-bearded Irishman in a kindly way. "Do ye hear from any of them?"

Banjo Mike shook his head.

"'Tis a sad thing when we have parted company with our own flesh and blood, Mike—'tis sad indeed. A mon has nothing——"

"Oh, yes," Banjo Mike said, quickly. "I've still got enough sense to get a laugh out o' blamed fools chasin' gold up and down the Rockies, Donald. If all the gold in this river was divided among 'em, it wouldn't be enough for a taste on the end of each man's tongue. An' I've got friends among the Indians, Donald . . . as you know."

Donald Ross nodded, and smiled thinly.

"Indeed ye have, Mike. Sometimes I wonder if ye haven't a little of the Beaver blood in your own veins, ye know them so well."

"I like Indians," Banjo Mike said. "While you are wearin' yerself out, Donald, for the damned Company you like so much, and for only a very small wage at that, I've got my banjo an' my friends . . . Why don't you write to the damned

Company in London, Donald, and tell 'em what a rotten thing it is!"

Donald Ross laughed.

"Each time you tell me that, Mike . . . Why don't I? There must be some reason why I don't . . . But to speak of something else, Mike—where the devil is Dan? I thought he'd be back in three days."

Banjo Mike had been wondering about this, too; but he said nothing. Either Dan or Joe was necessary for his trading during the fall; and he must decide soon which of the two it would be. He preferred Dan; yet he had no idea where Dan had gone, and he knew where he could find Joe.

Donald Ross was preparing to return to Fort Vermilion to arrange for supplies for the fall trading season and for the early spring when the Indians would come with many skins; but he decided to wait with Banjo Mike for another day or two, just in case Dan should show up.

They waited for two days, but there was no sign of Dan. Finally they put up a cache in Dan's abandoned tent, with ammunition and knives and some tobacco. There was a half bag of flour at the trading post, and they divided this, pouring half into a box which they left in Dan's tent with a note saying: "Follow us to Dunvegan. There is space for you in the next boat, and there is no longer any trouble with the miners."

Donald Ross signed the note, not knowing exactly how well Dan could read, although he had often seen the giant black man poring over his Bible.

On the third morning after the miners left, the two pushed off into the river with their canoes, heading downstream toward Dunvegan. At the same time Dan Williams was plunging through the marshes that lay to the west of the river, fighting mosquitoes and pausing every few miles to kneel in the soggy mattress of the forest to pray to the Lord to provide him with a cup in whatever mysterious way He chose.

It was a wonderful time of the year. The early summer sun had made the earth warm and mellow; and there were birds in the air and plenty of small game, including rabbit that had grown fat from summer feeding. Dan had enough venison and strips of cooked bear meat to last for days; but he also knew that if he wanted fresh meat, he had only to aim his gun and dinner was as good as served.

Dan had not kept count of the days since he left the Peace River; but on a certain day he found himself slogging down through the flat lowlands that rose gradually to the west of the river, and he knew he was not many miles from the place across from Fort St. John, where he had buried his canoe.

Dan was a bit ashamed of his attitude toward the Lord. He had sung only a few hymns, and except for intermittent prayers when he stopped to rest, he had not praised God sufficiently to merit any real attention. Yet he had every confidence that he would find the cup he needed so badly. He did not even know whether it was a weekday or Sunday when he first saw the Peace River again; but he knew that the Lord had His book up in the sky, and He knew how to keep records. The Reverend Sam had made that plain years ago when he called upon the members of his little flock to testify about their sins; and when Dan had wondered why the Lord needed this testimony, if He already knew everything that was going on, the Reverend Sam—as if divining this insurgence—had aimed a trembling finger directly at Dan and said:

"De Lord don' need your testimony, sinnahs—but yo' sho' needs de Lord!"

That was exactly the way Dan felt now; he needed the Lord, and he was sure the Lord would understand his need and forgive his sins. This was a simple and satisfactory doctrine that he had come to understand: the Lord always forgave people; all you had to do was hurry up and repent, and forgiveness would follow at once. Then the sinner would feel like a new man, which was the way Dan felt whenever he got down on his knees and prayed.

Dan reached the river early in the morning, and since he was tired, he decided to sleep. It was several hours later when he awakened, and only then because of the mosquitoes which had

85

clustered about him, droning in insectile ecstasy over the huge mound of living flesh.

Dan was hungry, but he was now so close to Fort St. John that he dared not make a fire, and shooting a rabbit was out of the question. He chewed on the strips of dried meat and drank water, leaning down over the shallow bank of a small stream feeding the Peace River and cupping the water in his hands. Then he crouched on his knees.

"Praise Jesus!" he exclaimed, in his deep, resonant voice. "Yo' child has come home again!"

He looked across the river to the place he had referred to as "home" and was surprised that he saw no smoke nor even any sign of life. He knew where the trader's house was located, and he could see it vaguely against the shadowy outline of the rising bluffs behind; but there was no smoke rising from it! And he could not see any canoes on the beach!

This was very strange. Dan wondered if they were out hunting for him, and he decided if this were the case, he would go into one of the huts while they were gone and take the cup he wanted. He might even leave a note explaining that he had borrowed it.

Dan was still some distance from the place where he had buried his canoe, and the night was coming on; he decided he would stay on the west side of the river for the night, and dig up his canoe and make the trip across to the camp the next morning.

The darkness came quickly, and all night it brooded over the empty river. Dan crouched on the riverbank, staring across the water and hoping to see a light. He felt a strange fear coming over him; he was now alone. He had never felt so much alone before, even when he was fleeing through the forest. He had counted on the Lord to lead him back to his friends, and now he was looking into the empty night, and his friends had gone.

The dawn brought light, but not in the mining camp across the river. There were no round blossoms of early morning fires; and no smoke spiraled up against the thin flush of dawn in the clear sky. Dan walked down the beach toward the promontory where he had buried his canoe. When he came closer and could see Fort St. John almost directly across the river, he could see clearly that there were no boats on the beach! And the tents were gone!

The blunt, brown shape of the small hill, upon which the log house of the Company store had been built, stood out against the green slope of the mountain. But the beach where the miners had pitched their tents was bare and deserted!

Dan wondered if they had moved their canoes somewhere, so he could not find them. Perhaps they were afraid he would come back and shoot up the camp. This idea filled him with a certain pride. He stood for some time, thinking about this; and he concluded that God must have forgiven him, or he would never have escaped as he did, and be able to return as a free man to a camp that had been deserted.

This latter notion brought back certain worries, including the feeling of being alone that he had experienced during the night. If the miners had left—even because they were afraid of Dan—there would still be no one to greet him when he came across the river. Dan decided he had better pray again, so he knelt down on the beach and said aloud:

"Sweet Jesus, Yo' tell them white folks Dan ain't goin' to shoot anybody! I jes' want to get back home!"

Dan found the place where he had hidden the canoe under a pile of spruce needles and leaves. He could see the outline of the pile easily, although it was beaten down from rains, and he quickly began to kick off the leaves and branches. His foot struck something hard, and he laughed. There it was—the canoe!

He dug his hand under the edge and tried to lift it, but the canoe was wedged fast in the pile of leaves. He raked more debris from the edge, and with a terrific heave managed to lift the canoe clear of the ground. Then he pulled out his cache of supplies which had been buried under the hull, and hoisted the canoe so he could get his head under it and carry it down to the river.

87

He was surprised to see daylight shining through the bottom of the canoe. He unshipped his burden and examined it more closely. The bark was swarming with ants.

Dan roared in anger, and with a great sweep of his hand struck the side of the canoe, sending out a shower of powdery wood and ants in a spray. He looked more closely, and then he knew what had happened. All the joints had been eaten away. The tallow had tightened and the seams were open.

For some time he stared at the remnants of his canoe. A swarm of ants had stopped him from crossing the river to see his friends! Dan looked at the canoe and then across the river. Even if his friends were still there, he could not reach them. For a while Dan's mind was blank; he could think of nothing to do. He had reached the river, expecting to cross it, and now suddenly a swarm of ants had changed everything. He was about to curse the ants when he suddenly remembered that they were God's creatures, and in some way the Lord must be responsible for this.

"I sho' ain't goin' to pray," he said aloud, with conviction. "The Lord must of done this an' I ain't goin' to say nothin' 'til I find out why He done it to me."

This was as close as Dan ever came to religious insurrection; yet it was not the first time he had resented some unexpected and unnatural interference of the Lord. On many occasions he had doubted the wisdom of the Lord—particularly when it seemed to have defeated Dan's own purposes. At these times he would mutter his objections aloud; and though he would usually repent at a later time, and pray for forgiveness, it did not necessarily imply his acceptance of these strange obstacles that the Lord threw in his path.

This time he did not even let God understand by prayer how bad he felt about the ants. Dan was, in a way, disappointed in the Lord. He walked down to the edge of the river, and aimed his gun into the air and fired it. Then his great voice rolled across the river:

"Here I is—come an' fetch me! Dan'l Williams! I come back, yo' hear! I come back! Come an' fetch me. . . ."

88

The sound of his voice echoed across the Peace River, but there was no sound or movement on the opposite bank. There was a terrible ring of fear in Dan's bellowing voice, and the more Dan shouted, the more afraid he became.

Finally he sat down. He had shouted so much that he was hoarse; and he had no more desire to call to his friends. It was at this point that he saw the figures of three men standing at the edge of a cluster of willow trees, perhaps a hundred yards away.

CHAPTER EIGHT

The men were watching Dan, silently. At first he thought they might be from the camp across the river; then he realized that they wore almost no clothes, so they must be Indians. They were incredibly dirty. The upper parts of their bodies appeared to be smeared with mud that had dried and caked.

The sight of men filled Dan with new confidence. He was no longer alone on the Peace River.

He stood up, and for perhaps a minute remained standing, looking at the silent spectators. The three men also remained motionless, staring at Dan. There was neither welcome nor hostility in their faces. There was not even an expression of curiosity. They merely stared.

Dan finally started walking toward them, his white teeth flashing in a friendly grin. He did not speak, because he was sure these Indians would not understand his language. But his deep laugh rolled out of his massive mouth, and he lifted one hand in a kind of apologetic greeting.

When he was ten steps from the trio, one of the Indians gave a yell and turned and ran into the thicket. His panic must have been great, because he did something that few Indians do: he stumbled and sprawled headlong into the brush, where he lay flat on the ground.

Dan had no way of knowing that the color of his skin had startled and frightened the Indian—as it had Attalu and his braves. All his life he had been black, and it was no novelty for men to look at him. But the color of his skin had never before provoked fear.

The two companions of the fallen warrior vanished into the brush as silently as they had come. Dan scarcely saw them go;

one instant they were there, and the next there was no one there except the Indian who had stumbled and was now lying on the ground, his black, burning eyes fixed on Dan.

Dan approached the fallen Indian, who had turned partly on his side. He was obviously a young brave, and his face showed more curiosity than might have been the case with an older warrior. But there is only one way for an Indian to die, and that is calmly and without fear; and the warrior's face showed no fear.

Dan knew one Indian expression; and he said the words slowly:

"Nila Usku-di-gio!"

It was an expression of peace and good will; and Dan, at this sudden restoration of human contact, felt peace and good will toward everyone. He held out his hand. The young Indian at first seemed to have no idea of the black giant's intentions. Here was a huge black spirit, whose powers were unquestionably beyond anything a Beaver brave had ever known; and all the Indian could know was that the black spirit was approaching him with an outstretched hand.

Dan leaned over and grasped the Indian's hand and tugged him to his feet. The Indian stood for some time without speaking. Dan turned away and observed that the two warriors who had vanished were now peering at him from the thicket. It was well known, of course, that a spirit could destroy a man merely by pointing at him; and they possibly expected their companion to shrivel under the force of Dan's gesture. It was also known that a man could not touch a spirit; yet this black spirit could be touched!

When Dan pulled the young Indian to his feet, the curiosity that had been sealed in the faces of all three Indians now broke forth. They stared at Dan with unabashed wonder.

The fact that Dan was neither an Indian nor a white man—although apparently of human origin—placed him in a strange class. There would be no honor in killing him. Had he been an Indian, he would have been a scout sent out by a neighboring tribe, and the rules of caution would have counseled them to

91

kill him so that he would never return to tell his people of anything he had seen. A white man, of course, would have been allowed to go without even knowing the Indians had seen him, since white men notoriously were foolish and usually saw nothing of importance anyway.

But a black man was something unprecedented; and no course of action was indicated. The only thing for the braves to do was to wait and see what happened.

Dan, on the other hand, had no such schooling. He was so full of delight at the sudden discovery that there were other human beings in the area that he could not restrain his exuberance. He broke again into a laugh and waved his great arms, and then began to talk volubly in English, which the Beavers understood only slightly.

He threw in a few Beaver words which he had learned in the camp at Fort St. John and from the scouts on the trip to Fort Vermilion. The Beavers are not a garrulous people; but their language is such that even those who understand it will fail to comprehend what Beaver braves are saying to each other. And their only encounters with those who spoke freely were the missionaries, who talked a great deal but said little that the Beavers could understand.

It was apparent that this huge black man was in some way related to the missionaries; otherwise he would not talk so much. But Dan's laughter and his wide grin, exposing a row of glistening white teeth, was of a slightly different character; this served to puzzle the Beaver braves even more.

The young man who had stumbled and fallen was Wapahu, or White Owl, which meant that he was very clever at appearing and disappearing swiftly without a sound, like a white owl. He was one of three scouts sent out by Komaxala to find out what Attalu and his band of exiled followers were planning.

They had tracked Attalu along the Peace River, and knew exactly who was with him and where they were encamped. On the way back they had observed from across the river the exodus from Fort St. John. They had witnessed the arrival of

Jacques Pardonet and his departure with the flotilla; and they had seen the Hudson's Bay trader, Donald Ross, and the red-haired man, Banjo Mike, whom they knew, leave in their canoes, pointed downstream.

But the sight of this black man was a new and strange experience. They had seen him when he returned to the Peace River, and had watched him dig up the canoe, which had been needlessly exposed to the ants. And then they observed him shooting his rifle aimlessly, and roaring strange words across the river at the empty beach on the other side.

One of the young warriors, Pamota, had lived as a young boy with a trapper who saved him from drowning and kept him in his hut in the forest. For this reason Pamota understood many things about white men that were known to only a few Beavers—perhaps to Komaxala, and to Ikta, the most powerful medicine man among the Beavers.

Pamota and Osawask, the third of the Beaver braves, had fled into the thicket at the approach of Dan; and now as Dan stood chattering with Wapahu in a combination of English and Beaver words, none of which made sense, Pamota racked his brain for recollections from his youthful days with the trapper that might explain this black apparition.

Pamota had acquired a reputation after his return from many years spent with the trapper; and it was not an enviable one. He had spoken of houses taller than the trees of the forest, and long council houses that moved swiftly across the land carrying many people, and black rocks that burned like wood! All these things had given him the evil name of a man with a forked tongue among the Beaver braves. Nevertheless, he was known as a good warrior and a youth of great promise as a hunter; consequently, instead of killing him, the Beaver braves merely ordered him to remain silent and tell no more lies which would bring disgrace upon the Beaver tribe.

Now he advanced toward Dan and extended his hand. Dan was so delighted at this friendly approach that he took the young Beaver's hand in a crushing grip; but Pamota, although the bones of his hand seemed about to crack, made no grimace

93

of pain; he merely looked stolidly at the black man. It was known that if a man touched the hand of a spirit, his hand would go through the other as if it were air; and now that Pamota as well as Wapahu had grasped the hand of the black man, all three of the young braves understood immediately that Dan must be human, even though he was black.

Pamota signaled to the other two, and it was understood between them that the black man had come in peace; there was to be no act of violence against him until they had given the matter further consideration—probably not until the entire affair had been reported to Komaxala.

The three young Indians made their attitude known to Dan through signs and a few words in English which Pamota could speak. Then they examined the canoe. It was quickly evident that the damage done by the ants could be repaired.

Pamota pointed across the river, and said to Dan:

"No white man!"

Dan understood for the first time that Fort St. John had been abandoned during his flight into the hills. It was disheartening to realize that Banjo Mike and Donald Ross had deserted him; nevertheless he resolved to cross the river and see if he could find a cup.

Wapahu indicated by signs, with the aid of Pamota's sparse English, that he needed marrow to calk the canoe. Dan took his gun and headed into the forest. This was a task to his liking. Wapahu followed him, either to assist or perhaps to see that Dan did not continue to walk through the forest away from them!

They reached a small brook where grass grew along the bank, and Wapahu silently signaled that here they would find a deer.

At the first glade there was no sign of deer, but Wapahu, gliding silently through the trees, signaled for Dan to follow. Dan did not understand any of the short words Wapahu had uttered in the Beaver tongue, but he knew what each signal meant. He understood the Indian, even though they could not speak to each other; and this gave Dan a wonderful sense of being together with someone. He remembered how he had prayed to the Lord during the night to have someone light a fire on the other side of the river, just to show that there were other people around; and Dan decided that this was God's answer to his prayer.

The sun was overhead when they saw a large deer, perhaps a quarter of a mile away. The animal raised its head, as if it smelled something. Wapahu stood motionless, and after a while Dan leaned forward and peered through the brush. Then he saw what he had not observed before: there was not one deer but a small herd; and the deer they spotted was a buck which stood a little way from the rest, watching over them with that silent responsibility that is part of the instinct of animals. Now and then the buck would toss his head, as if he had observed something; but the Indian knew this was only the habit of the deer, to reassure the herd that the buck was on guard.

Wapahu carried an old muzzle-loader, and Dan knew the Indian could not hit the deer from that distance. They advanced closer, but the buck suddenly became alert. Wapahu stopped and raised his hand to show Dan that he did not believe it would be possible to kill the deer from that distance. He stood, holding his gun at his side. There was already defeat in his attitude when Dan raised his Sharps and fired almost in a single motion. The noise crashed through the forest, and the herd galloped off as if stung. But the big buck took only a step or two and then pitched forward.

Wapahu raised his gun and fired at the running pack, but it was too late. His bullet whistled aimlessly through the trees and the little herd disappeared.

Dan broke into a great laugh. Wapahu stared at the black man, but he said nothing. It was not the custom for an Indian to shout loudly over an animal he had killed. In battle, an Indian would shout in advance, to terrify or disconcert his enemy. But when a feat had been accomplished, it was wise to remain silent and let others observe the skill with which it was done. Any word or gesture of praise, coming even grudgingly from another, was worth a thousand words of self-praise.

Dan did not understand this; possibly he would not have cared about it if he had understood it. He had proved once more his mastery with a gun; and it was as natural as breathing that he should laugh boastfully. It was simply his way of expressing his pleasure.

They went quickly about the business of skinning the deer, the Indian working silently and Dan chattering loudly in English, with a word of Beaver now and then.

"The Lord sho' makes Dan shoot straight," he observed, ripping away the skin and exposing the raw, purple wound where the bullet had struck the deer. "Yo' is a heathen, an' yo' ain't got no idea of what the Lord can do when He wants to—forgivin' sinners an' takin' care o' his own child'en . . . Praise the Lord!"

They cut the meat away from the back and split the bones, taking out the marrow and pressing it into a ball. Then they took the heart and tongue and enough meat for their immediate needs and returned to the shore of the river where Pamota and Osawask were working on the canoe.

Dan gathered wood to make a fire, in order to broil the meat; but Osawask, which means Yellow Bear, paid no attention to the wood Dan gathered. Instead he drew several pieces of dry willow from the thicket.

Dan stared at him, thinking that possibly the Indian had not seen the wood he gathered. Then he turned to Pamota and said, *"Tan si maka?"*—which meant "What's the matter?"

Pamota said nothing for a moment; then he said in English:

"Make fire with no smoke. At night see big fire from many places. In day only smoke. So Indian make little fire with no smoke."

Dan shrugged. It seemed rather pointless to him to worry about who would see the fire; but he knew the ways of Indians were strange, so he let Osawask build the fire, and he began to lay out pieces of venison to broil.

Osawask meanwhile laid a heavy round log over the burning splinters, at an angle so that the wind would blow under it and the fire would eat through the wood from the bottom. Thus it burned slowly, without showing much flame above the wood; yet the heat was as strong as a blazing fire would have been. Such a fire might last all night, and in the morning it could be revived merely by blowing on the smoldering embers under the log. But these were things of which Dan knew nothing.

That night the three Indians and the black man remained on the western shore of the river. The next morning they finished melting the marrow until it made a paste that was spread over the edges of the bark. This formed a gluelike covering which made the hull sound and watertight.

The four then paddled over to the other side, but when they arrived there was no sound of voices or sign of life. The camp was gone, the tents pulled up, and only the log house of the Hudson's Bay Company trader and a few wooden huts remained.

Dan wasted little time, after they pulled the canoe ashore, in making an inspection of the camp site. While the Indians dragged the canoe up on the beach, he started with long strides toward the factor's house. His own tent was behind it, and he went there first. On the ground was a pile of things, including a box to which a note had been fastened. Dan took the note and carefully spelled out the words aloud: "Follow us to Dunvegan . . . no longer trouble with miners."

Dan threw back his head and laughed. The sound carried easily to the beach, where the Indians had left the canoe and were climbing up the hill to the factor's house. They stopped, looking at each other. It seemed that again the strange black man had violated all rules of caution by bellowing in this meaningless way, which would give notice to anyone within hearing distance that there were men at the empty village of the white men.

Dan looked over the supplies left by Banjo Mike and Donald Ross. There was a box of bullets for his rifle, and tobacco and flour and tea. There was also a frying pan and a tin cup. He laughed again, while the three Indians, who had come up silently to the door of the tent, stared at him.

Dan came out where the Indians were standing. He felt that he was a great man now. He made a sign that he was going up to the log house, and the Indians followed. Inside the trader's house there were many other things—stores that Donald Ross had left, knowing that only a traveler needing food and shelter would touch anything. The Indians for hundreds of miles around would pass the house and not enter it. They knew it was the post of the Hudson's Bay Company, whose long arm could reach all the way from London into the wilderness and punish anyone who transgressed its property.

Now the Indians stood outside the door and listened to Dan. He talked to himself, muttering words that sounded strange even to Pamota's ears. Finally they peered in, and witnessed a strange sight. The black man was on his knees, holding his hands in front of his forehead, muttering, "Sweet Jesus, Yo' done foun' peace for Yo' sinnin' chil' . . . Yo' done led Dan outen the wild'ness. . . ."

After Dan had completed his expressions of piety and penitence, which he felt would cause the Lord to forgive his momentary doubts when he stood earlier on the riverbank and shouted for his friends, he rose and came out of the house. He saw the three Indians, standing there, looking at him silently.

"I has jes' talked with Jesus," he said quietly. "Some day ef'n yo' follows the word of God, yo' will be able to talk to Him . . . like me."

Dan felt refreshed at this idea. It seemed to put him almost in a class with the missionaries, who carried the word of God into such remote places as this and made the heathen Indians —and presumably sinners like himself—into Christians.

It struck Dan that God might have caused him to miss his friends at Fort St. John for this purpose—so that he might spread the word of the Lord among the Indians, the way missionaries did, according to stories the Reverend Sam had told back in Georgia.

Filled with this new purpose, he walked around the camp

paying little attention to the Indians, who stood and watched, observing each action. Dan now felt that he had become a man of real importance; and when he saw some cups in one of the permanent huts abandoned by the miners, he took them down from the hooks on which they hung and put them with the other supplies in his cache.

Now he was indeed a man of importance—with four cups! The Lord had really taken care of him. Dan felt like kneeling down again to thank God, but he felt that this excessive demonstration of thanksgiving might weaken the impression he would have made with his long prayer, not only on God but on the three Indians. He contented himself with pointing to the cups and saying:

"Dan now got four cups," and with sudden magnanimity, he handed one cup to each Indian. The fourth, together with the one Banjo Mike had left for him, would give him a regular cup and a spare, which was all any man could ask.

Now that Dan knew no one had the right to command him, he became very happy, and even looked with a certain amount of arrogance on the Indians; It was entirely up to him, he decided, whether to remain at Fort St. John, where he had plenty of supplies, and hunt and perhaps trap game during the winter; or whether to go with the Indians to their village, where there would be plenty of people and where he would undoubtedly be respected as a great man.

Wapahu, Pamota, and Osawask continued to watch Dan, saying little to him or to each other. The Indians had observed fresh mounds where the white men had put three of their fellows into the ground and planted sticks over them, which was foolish, of course, since the sticks would attract the attention of enemies who might use this knowledge to harass their spirits in the hunting grounds beyond the edge of the sky.

Dan had brought the remaining venison across the river in the canoe, and now he decided he would bake some bread with the flour and make a great dinner, with a fire in the stone cooking place near his tent. None of the Indians objected to the fire; they were at the camp of the white men, where all rules were abandoned, and they merely sat and watched while Dan prepared a dinner after his own fashion.

Dan laughed as he cooked, and since he could not talk very well with the Indians, he talked to himself. This was now his place—his "home." It was the first time in his life he had ever "owned" anything, and he began to talk to himself about the great time he would have during the winter, living in his own place. He even thought of building a church where he could say his prayers. It struck him that it might be lonely in the church by himself; he thought perhaps he could get the Indians to stay with him, and he would make Christians and repentant sinners out of them.

While he was meditating on these matters, he saw a moose swimming across the river. No one knows why a moose swims across a river, even against a strong current. Perhaps it is to get away from wolves, or even mosquitoes; or it might be that the smell of herbs fills the air with temptation.

Osawask was the first to see it, and when he pointed to the head of the moose, which was still some distance out on the river, Dan picked up his rifle and, without seeming to aim, shot the moose in the head. It floundered around a bit, and the Indians rushed to the canoe, paddling out on the river where the dying moose lay half submerged. They towed it in; it was enough meat to feed the whole Beaver village.

Pamota mentioned this, and Dan immediately suggested that the people of the Beaver village come to Fort St. John as his guests. This Pamota knew would be impossible, but another idea struck him, which was not so impossible.

"You great hunter," he said. "Maybe you come to Beaver village."

Perhaps, Dan thought, it would be better to go with the Indians, and teach them from his Bible in their own village. In that way he would always be a great man, and no white man could order him to do anything he did not want to do.

He quickly made up his mind. He took as much of the supplies left by Banjo Mike and Donald Ross as he would need for his own use, as well as a few things for gifts; when everything was finished he closed the door to the trading post and drew three crosses on the door.

This, he explained to the Indians, meant that it was the house of a Christian and that God would protect everything within the house. After this they loaded the canoe with as much meat as they could carry, together with tobacco and tea and flour, and headed downriver toward the village of the Beavers.

CHAPTER NINE

It was remarkable how rapidly Dan learned to communicate with the three young Indians. At first a few vocables were understood; then common interests made their words and gestures intelligible to each other. Although each knew only a few words of the other's language, good will made the difference; and since Indians are not very talkative, and accompany most words with some movement of the hands, it was not long before they understood each other.

There were some things, of course, that Dan never understood. These were passed by word or sign among the Indians. At night one of them invariably would leave camp, and after some time would return, saying nothing to Dan of the reason for the absence. They seldom brought back anything in the way of game, and although he asked about these strange goings and comings, he never received any satisfactory reply.

After they had gone downriver a short distance in Dan's canoe, they beached it and loaded all they could carry on their backs. Then the Indians struck off inland, across a sloping mountain which jutted out into the Peace River. They had to walk some distance before they could ascend the ridge of this mountain, and Dan found the same clouds of mosquitoes along the low, swampy land that he had found when he fled from Fort St. John a few weeks before. However, it was more pleasant on the higher land, until they came down on the other side where they again ran into swampy country, covered with grassy mounds that did not offer very sure footing.

The three Indians leaped easily from one mound to the next, always seeming to know exactly where to put their feet; but Dan lumbered through the soggy soft spots, hauling his feet laboriously out of one slimy patch and into another. He soon became wet and discouraged. Now and then he slipped and fell, and the Indians looked at him, obviously amused. This annoyed Dan, because he felt it removed him from the pinnacle of importance he had gained at Fort St. John. He even stopped now and then to mutter a short prayer, asking God to see to it that he did not stumble. This made little change in his progress, so Dan quit praying.

They reached a stretch of low ground where the mounds of hard earth seemed to be floating, like logs lying resiliently in the mud. Dan lost his balance several times. He carried his gun in one hand and a teakettle in the other; this did not make it any easier to balance himself. The bundle tied to his back was heavy, and threw him off balance. After jumping from mound to mound, he decided the water might not be too deep, and he began to wade recklessly through the soggy marsh pools.

This was a mistake. After a few steps, he found one foot sucked deep in the mud, and he could not pull it out. Dan tried to drag the leg free, using all his great strength; instead he twisted around and plunged into the swamp water.

He tried to break his fall, putting out one hand. This caused him to drop the teakettle. His fist gripped the end of a grassy mound, but this gave way and he found himself slipping down the side into the water. His face sank into the water, and he began to thresh his arms in panic, abandoning his gun in an effort to lift himself out of the sucking slime.

The more he twisted, the deeper he seemed to go; then the mud began to choke him. The weight of the pack on his back added to the burden, and his hands, plunging into the mud, could not reach anything solid enough to hold him up so that he could breathe.

Dan did not know where the three Indians were, but he could hear the voice of one calling to the others. He tried to shout for them to come and pull him out, but the water choked him. The black mud was engulfing his body, and he felt a wild fear. He tried to shout again, but when he opened his mouth he swallowed more of the muddy water.

Indians notoriously are fatalists; and it is possible that the three Indians, observing their comrade floundering in the mud, decided it was the way of the Great Spirit, reducing the boasting black man to a dying animal. Finally, Pamota slipped his pack from his shoulders and in a few nimble leaps reached the mound where Dan lay, sinking deeper and deeper into the mire.

Pamota took a solid foothold on the edge of the mound, reached out and gripped Dan's shoulder, and rolled him over. Then he scraped the mud from Dan's face and mouth with his fingers. Dan's eyes rolled wildly in the mask of black slime, and he coughed and choked but could utter no words.

Pamota saw to it that enough mud was raked off Dan's face and out of his mouth to enable him to breathe, and then he stooped and dragged the body of the black man toward the hard ground. When Dan was half out of the mud, Pamota and the others, who had come up to help him, began to beat him on the back to force the water out of his lungs.

Dan was weak and only half conscious when they finally got him in condition to breathe freely again. He lay for some time, coughing and spitting up mud. When he was able to get to his feet, he looked miserable and abject, but the Indians said nothing. Each took up his burden again and they started across the bog, helping Dan until they reached higher ground. Finally they piloted him to the base of a cliff, and while he lay there, still gasping and coughing, they went back and picked up his bundle and rifle.

When they returned, the teakettle was missing; without a word Pamota turned and went back to the mound where Dan had lost it. He finally found the kettle and cover and brought them back to Dan. Still not one of the Indians had spoken to him.

Dan felt bad physically, but he felt worse in his mind. He was no longer a great man among them. The Indians had had to drag him from mud, and he knew he had lost face with

104

them. He leaned over, holding his head in his hands, and said aloud:

"Jesus in heaven—why Yo' done this to Dan? Why Yo' done let Yo' sheep fall into the mud, sweet Jesus?"

He even thought of taking direct issue with the Lord for having humiliated him in front of these Indians, since this would reduce his chance of converting them to Christianity. The Lord had made Dan's work in His behalf just that much harder, and he thought of mentioning this in a prayer, but something stopped him. In his present condition, Dan instinctively felt that he was in no position to strike a bargain with the Lord over his future missionary activities. He would have to leave that for a later prayer, when he was not covered with mud and half sick from the black water he had gulped into his stomach.

Dan's supplies had become badly damaged by the immersion. His tea was soggy, and had to be laid out on a rock to dry. The flour could be saved by throwing away the layer that caked around it, but the sugar was completely spoiled. While Dan spread his food out, trying to salvage what he could, and coughing and vomiting black water at intervals, the Indians built a fire so that he could dry his clothes and warm his shaking body.

Dan observed the Indians watching him when he pulled his clothes off, but he thought nothing of it. However, it seemed to be a matter of great interest to them. With curiosity, Pamota watched him scrape the mud off his chest and arms and legs and even came closer to inspect Dan's skin in the areas not usually revealed to other people's eyes.

Dan grinned, and made a special effort to let them see all of him so they would understand that he was black all over—not just in his face and hands.

The following day they would reach Komaxala's camp; but the three young Indians apparently were not certain of the reception they would get when they brought Dan into the camp, so they had sent up smoke signals to advise the Beavers that a stranger was with them. This enabled more experienced braves to come close to them and inspect the stranger, giving signals to the young Indians which were understood and answered, while Dan was unaware that anyone was watching him.

While they were sitting around the fire, Komaxala himself stepped into the circle of light. He was tall and powerful, and his face was like a mask etched in stone. He did not even greet the young Indians, who stood quietly at one side, but walked up to Dan and held out his hand, as Pamota had done.

Dan did not stand up, but remained sitting on a stone. He had no idea that this kind of conduct was insulting to a Beaver chief; he simply felt too tired to get to his feet.

"*Bo ju!*" Komaxala said.

He wished Dan to know that he was acquainted with the white man's language; but since Dan did not understand French—particularly the inflection of the Beaver tongue—he merely nodded and grinned, exhibiting a row of white teeth.

Komaxala's face darkened slightly, but he was a wise chief, not given to hasty decisions. He extended one arm, and several Beaver braves stepped into the light of the campfire.

When Dan saw himself surrounded by Indians, his eyes rolled from side to side, and he felt that he was no longer a great man. In fact, it was not impossible that the Indians might kill him.

He continued to smile, however, and explained as well as he could with the limited words at his disposal that he was ashamed of appearing in such a ridiculous way before the chief —with half his clothes still drying by the fire. He pointed to the tea on the rock, and said that this had been meant for Komaxala as a gift.

The Indian chief understood what Dan meant, and he raised his hand in appreciation. He understood enough of Dan's speech to be able to convey it to the others, and the attitude of the other Indians changed perceptibly. Some of them came closer to peer at Dan's black skin, and they exchanged looks between themselves.

Dan had washed his teacups, and now he boiled some tea

over the fire and filled the cups. Komaxala took one and indicated that Dan should drink from the other. In a slow speech, composed of a few English and Beaver words, the chief explained to Dan that he greatly appreciated the gift of tea. The Beavers had always had tea to drink with moose meat, which made it more tasty; but lately evil luck had befallen them and their young braves had taken to fighting with each other. He referred vaguely to Attalu, but said nothing definite, since no outsider should be allowed to learn of the dishonor in his tribe.

Dan drank his cup of tea and then indicated that he would like to wash the rest of the mud off his body so that he would not appear so badly. He went down to a small creek that ran under the cliff, and found a pool where he could wash himself. Komaxala and the others stared at him when he returned; finally Pamota spoke to the chief in the Beaver tongue, using words Dan could not understand.

After this a lean, old man who—as Dan later learned—was Ikta, the chief medicine man of the tribe, came close to Dan and pointed to his black chest.

"You wash not much good," he said.

Dan did not understand his meaning; he thought perhaps the old man referred to his clothes, which were still stained with mud.

"I goin' to clean 'em tomorrow," he said.

The old medicine man shook his head.

"Face not clean," he said distinctly. "White man face white. Indian face brown." He stopped significantly.

Dan grinned. He was used to having white people in the North notice his color, since there were not many colored men in the Peace River country. But he could think of nothing to say. He realized that this might be taken by the Indians to mean that he was ashamed of his color, so finally he said:

"I is a colored boy. Ain't yo' seen no colored folks before?"

Ikta stepped back. His lean face, etched with deep lines, showed grave disfavor. It was evident that he regarded Dan with suspicion, and Dan shook his head. His massive head rolled from side to side and his heavy mouth split in an apologetic grin.

"The Lord done made Dan black," he said finally, his deep, melodious voice rolling forth in a sudden burst of sound that startled the Indians. "God done made folks white an' yellow and black—an' red, like yo' Injuns!" He looked from face to face; and Komaxala, at this moment, stepped forward with his hand upraised.

"The black man has come in peace," he said to the others. "The white spirit has brought many victories to white men—and perhaps the black spirit also has brought victories to black men. There are among us those who have spoken with the medicine men of the white man, and they have told us of the power of the white man's god. Perhaps this man is black so that he cannot be seen at night. This would be wonderful if he could teach us this art as well."

Dan understood little of what Komaxala said, but it was evident the chief spoke in friendliness. He suddenly raised his voice in a hymn, and the Indians stood silently until he had finished, not knowing the purpose of the hymn but believing that it was the black man's way of speaking to his Great Spirit.

Osawask then stepped before the chief. He explained that during the time they had led the black man toward the Beaver camp, they had gone into the woods at night and left pieces of meat as sacrifices for the spirits; since the meat had been eaten, it was a sign that they were favored by the spirits. He spoke of the black man's great skill with a gun, which was loaded from the back end and could kill a moose at an incredible distance.

Komaxala nodded gravely; he had already received this information, but now it was presented in connection with the question Ikta had raised, and he wished it to be understood by all that he had received the black man in friendliness.

Komaxala gave orders to a couple of young braves, and they disappeared into the forest. He let it be known that the rest would remain at the camp until the next day and then return to the Beaver village. During the night the fire was kept burning by the younger braves, who tossed wood on it so that the flames spurted up—this was the land of the Beavers and there was no danger of enemies. Others stood outside the circle of fire, watching for animals that might be attracted by the flames.

Among the boys who tended the fire was one called Gnanisk, who was one of the fastest and strongest of the young braves. He was even stronger than many of the full-grown braves, and was foremost among the growing boys who would soon become warriors.

Gnanisk slipped away from the firelight and started to the forest. Another boy, Kichsibu, saw Gnanisk leave, and followed him. Kichsibu was the grandson of an old man who had been killed in the battle with Attalu's followers; and while it was known that Gnanisk had killed him, Kichsibu had never spoken about this to Gnanisk. Both were relatives of the chief, and were required to join in the celebration when Attalu and his followers were sent into exile; yet because the two boys had a deep friendship for each other, neither took my pleasure in the celebration.

Now when Gnanisk rose and left the fire, Kichsibu quickly overtook him in the forest. Gnanisk said he was going to get some wood, but Kichsibu knew that his friend had seen something in the forest. They walked deeper into the woods, each going in a different direction to avoid giving the impression that either one wished to spy on the other; yet Kichsibu knew that Gnanisk had gone for some purpose he had not revealed.

Actually, Gnanisk had gone into the forest to see if there might be a deer, or perhaps a black bear in the neighborhood; now it was necessary to make his excursion seem even more mysterious, so he quickly turned aside from the trail he had been following. Kichsibu continued for a short distance; then he had the feeling that someone else was near him. His eyes traveled constantly from side to side, even as he ran with soft, padded strides through the trees. Suddenly he saw a figure disappear behind some underbrush.

He could not see the figure clearly, so he stopped, remaining motionless so that the eyes of the other could not distinguish him from the trees around him. The other did not move, either; finally Gnanisk moved up to the bush quietly, and found an Indian boy, whom he knew, crouching behind the bush.

The other boy, whose name was Jonus, had seen that it was Kichsibu and had remained motionless so that at least only one figure could be seen moving through the woods if there should be an enemy nearby.

Jonus told him that a great number of white men had been seen going westward in canoes along the river; and Kichsibu quickly took Jonus back to the camp. Gnanisk already had returned to put wood on the fire—since it would have disgraced both boys if the fire had been allowed to die out—and they took Jonus to the place where Komaxala slept. The chief awakened at the first touch of the boy.

Komaxala lifted his hand and made a motion, which in sign language meant "Is it a bear?"

By similar movements of his hands, Jonus made it known to the chief that it was not a bear. Then he said in sign language that a large number of white men were moving through the western part of the land where the Beavers lived. Neither Komaxala nor the boy spoke aloud, and Komaxala scarcely raised his head. Quietly he slipped away from the fire and walked outside the circle of light. Jonus followed and when they reached a place far enough so that their voices could not be heard, Jonus told his chief the story.

Several large boats had been seen going upriver. In the biggest boat was the French trader, whom they knew. The party consisted of many white men who had lived on the river at the Hudson's Bay Company trading post. These men slept on shore each night, with huge fires burning, taking no precautions against attack. Jonus had been close to their camps and had counted the men; the most astonishing thing was that one of the men was not white but black.

It was necessary to wake up Ikta, who came to the place where Komaxala sat. He listened while Jonus again related what he had seen.

"It is possible that a tribe of black men is visiting this coun-

110

try," Ikta said finally. He recalled that when the white men first came to the land of the Beavers, they had come in small numbers; and if these had been killed, perhaps no others would have followed.

Now the white men were all over, each new arrival sending back to his homeland word of the richness of the Beaver country. Ikta suggested that perhaps the first of the black men now arriving would send back word to their people; perhaps the land of the Beavers would soon be full of white men and black men, and there would be no hunting left for the Indians.

"What shall we do?" he asked. "There are now so many white men that hardly a moon goes by that we do not see them going up or down the river."

Komaxala thought about this.

"We have had guns since the white man came," he said. "It is now easier to get meat. We also have knives, with which we can cut up the game more rapidly. We have needles finer and stronger than the finest needles of twisted sinew that we had before. Our women are very happy to have these needles and the thread which the white man brings. We have tobacco . . ."

Ikta raised a hand.

"The manners of our women are worse—like the manners of the squaws of the white men. They decorate themselves with pieces of cloth and they gossip because their time is no longer occupied with work."

Komaxala had never known a time when he did not understand that there were other kinds of people to be found in the world, people different from the Indians of his tribe and other Indian tribes. But this was not true of Ikta. He was older, but he had never learned to understand or accept the new life that had come with the white man.

Now the question arose, Would the black men bring peace or war? Komaxala had heard from the three young braves who brought the great black man with them that this man had not been warlike; on the contrary he had been so peaceful and friendly that he had followed them through the swamps and fallen into the mud.

111

If these white men, traveling through the Beaver country, had a black man among them—who did not seem to be traveling as a captive—was it not a sign that the black men came in peace, and not as enemies?

The two Indians exchanged their views with motions of the hand, a slight inclination of the head, and now and then a few words. The main thing, Komaxala told the medicine man, was not to make enemies of those who might prove more powerful than the Beavers—as the white men had proved.

Ikta's grave expression hardened with dislike whenever white men were mentioned, and now the black man was added to this hatred.

Komaxala finally rose and signaled that he had made his decision. The black stranger was to be treated as a guest and regarded as a chief among his own people. The order would be given to Kanipaw, one of the elders of the tribe who had remained at the village: Peace ruled over the land of the Beavers, and whoever disobeyed the order of peace would invoke Komaxala's anger.

Komaxala mentioned also that the stories of the three young braves had indicated that this black warrior had a special talent, which could bring food to the tribe. When he spoke with his long rifle, he always hit whatever he aimed at. Such a guest was good to have.

The two returned to camp, and Komaxala addressed Dan.

"Black man," he said, "we are going to our summer home. It will be one day traveling. Meanwhile, some game may cross our path, and if so we will stop to kill the game. Our people have been troubled by great events, and our stores of meat are not large. It will help much to have the storing places filled as soon as possible!"

Dan grinned, and patted his long Sharps rifle. This was the kind of talk he understood. He immediately took his gun apart and cleaned it thoroughly, brushing away the dirt that had caked around the breechloading chamber and drawing a fiber with rags tied to it through the gun barrel until it was shining inside.

112

After he had put the rifle together, he noticed a small squirrel in a tree some distance away.

Dan pointed a long black finger at the squirrel.

"Yo' see that squirrel?" he asked Komaxala. The Indian nodded, but he indicated by a movement of his hand that the squirrel was not in danger at that distance. It would be a waste of powder and lead, and since failure was certain, it would be foolhardy to try it.

Dan took careful aim and fired. The squirrel dropped from the branch. Dan looked around at the Indians who were standing near him, and then he threw back his head and laughed. The Indians showed no surprise, and Komaxala merely regarded Dan carefully. Here was a man who liked to brag; and that was good to know.

Dan looked around, seeking some recognition of his feat. He decided he had better drive the lesson home.

"Anybody here like to shoot against Dan?" he asked in a loud voice. "I got some tobacco that says Dan can outshoot anybody!"

The words of the challenge were not understood by many, but the meaning was clear. Dan stood with his gun under his arm, laughing with delight. These Indians would soon find out what a marksman he was! He reminded himself, in passing, that all this would be to the credit of the Lord, since it would prove He was a stronger God than the spirits of the Indians. He decided he would bring this to the attention of the Lord when he next prayed, thus ensuring some heavenly support when he needed to shoot with extreme fineness.

Ikta, who had watched the demonstration of shooting, now held up his hand.

"No waste bullet on small game," he told Dan. "One bullet —one moose, one bear. Many times bigger than squirrel!"

Komaxala turned to the braves and with a motion of his hand gave the order to break camp and proceed to the home of the Beavers. Dan turned to his own supplies, collecting the tea, which was still damp, and tobacco which also had been spread out and seemed to have dwindled during the night.

H 113

The Indians moved into the forest, spreading across a wide area in such a way that each brave walked alone; yet all were constantly in contact. Komaxala walked at the head of a small group of Indians, with Dan just behind him.

Now and then a brave would step close to Komaxala and receive some kind of instructions; then shortly the brave would drift out into the woods and disappear. No noise betrayed the passage of these Indians through the forests. They moved as silently as the wind, following the directions of their chief. The messengers of Komaxala were already far up the river or moving inland or toward the high mountains to the west and south, calling the Beaver chiefs and elder warriors into council.

Important events were in the making, and no single warrior of the Beaver tribe knew exactly what plans Komaxala harbored.

CHAPTER TEN

The village of the Beaver Indians was situated on a shelf of land above a lake as calm and clear as a mirror. Along the beach were fish scaffolds from the previous year, gaunt skeletons of an earlier prosperity. Now they were empty of fish; there was not even the smell of fish or of any animal. No one was in the village when they arrived.

The braves filtered out of the forest into the village clearing, walking among the huts which were spread out in a disorderly array. Piles of garbage and the remains of last year's living were scattered aimlessly between the huts.

Dan sat down on the ground among the Indians, completely exhausted by the walking and the strange things he had seen and experienced. He said very little to anyone, because it was difficult to make himself understood; the others were equally silent, looking out into the empty spaces of the lake or stretching out on the grass to sleep.

The women had not yet arrived in the camp, and none of the braves would lift a hand to set anything in order. This was work for women, and except for a muttered word now and then about the "laziness" of the women, there was no effort to put anything in order.

A few of the younger braves started a gambling game. Wapahu was the organizer of the game, something in the manner of a dealer. He arranged some sticks of wood of varying lengths and colors on a blanket, which he spread across his knees. Some of the sticks were scraped clean; others had rings cut in them; and others had the bark still on them.

Each player placed in front of him the articles he wished to risk in the gambling: blankets, pearls, bits of cloth and even food; it was immediately evident which braves were willing to risk their best possessions and which were gambling only small things of little worth.

One of the braves began to chant a song, in a singsong voice, and this attracted others. Old Ikta, the medicine man, sat a little distance away, giving no sign that he knew what was going on; finally he arose and plucked a large pearl, which was dangling from one ear, out of its fastening and tossed it toward the ring of gamblers, indicating that he was a player in the game.

When all who wanted to play had joined the circle, the chanting song ceased abruptly. Wapahu gathered the sticks under a fold of the blanket. Old Ikta, by right of seniority, was the first to guess the number of sticks under the fold; and his guess was exactly the number Wapahu had counted out.

The old medicine man reached toward the pile and took his own pearl earring. Then he rummaged through the pile and picked out a good knife. His withered face was like a mask, but his eyes showed his scorn of the younger braves. By his gestures he showed them what was in his mind: that these young braves were too inexperienced to make the game any kind of sport for him. He had merely wished to show them how easily he could win.

"I have taken the knife of Kwolsit," he finally said, "because it was his only knife, and he deserved to lose it . . . I might have taken a prize from the others, who have more than Kwolsit. But I wished the loss to be felt. That is why I took his most prized possession."

This was a clever speech. It was spoken with the loftiness of wisdom; it was not the speech of a braggart; yet it had the elements of self-praise and of disdain. At the conclusion of his comments, Ikta turned his cold eyes toward Dan. Then he arose and left the group.

Kwolsit also arose, having nothing left to wager, and walked a little way off from the group. His face expressed neither disappointment nor anger. He sat down on the grass and waited for the game to end.

Dan looked at the defeated gambler, and he felt a sudden impulse of pity. He would have offered Kwolsit some of his own possessions; but at this moment a woman walked into the enclosure, waddling into sight among the irregular lanes of huts. She was enormous, and her fat body rolled as she walked. Her face, red from exposure, was a mask of ugliness. Dan had never seen an Indian woman as fat and as unpleasant to look upon as this new arrival. She panted at each step as if it were her last; and her black eyes, peering from the folds of her face, seemed to rake the squatting gamblers with unspoken contempt and disgust.

She did not speak to anyone, nor did any of the men appear to notice her. She walked to one of the huts and looked into it, without entering. Then she turned and deposited her enormous bulk with a rolling motion on the grass, near a large log that had been blown over by the wind. With her back resting against this log, she unloosed a torrent of remarks, none of which Dan understood—except that she was undoubtedly quite angry, and quite contemptuous.

None of the men replied to her, or even took notice of her.

After a while she seemed to sink into the bulk of her body, her short neck almost disappearing in the immense shoulders. She had no trouble keeping her balance, spread out as she was upon the grass; and for a while it seemed as if she had gone to sleep.

Suddenly she broke out again in a torrent of abuse, yelling: "*A hai! A hai!*" Dan understood enough of the Beaver language to know that she was addressing someone as a "stupid man . . . a lazy, good-for-nothing."

He saw a man walking slowly into the village, carrying a burden on his shoulders. His head was almost hidden by the huge bundle, and his steps faltered as if he were about to collapse from exhaustion.

This was Tyentegen, who, as Dan learned later, had long since lost all importance as a hunter, or even as a man. He was the laughingstock of the tribe—a man who suffered the abuse of his wife. The others looked at him with amusement

117

and contempt; and his wife, Sagafewah, the fat lady who had preceded his entrance, treated him not only with contempt but with physical abuse. Her name, literally translated, meant Sunrise; but there was little in her actions or appearance to inspire any poetical allusions to her name. She alone of the women of the tribe walked through the forest with no burden; her husband carried their belongings. He did the cooking, cleaned the cooking utensils, repaired the tent and their clothing, and took care of the dogs.

In spite of his descent from the lordly position of a warrior and a man, the old man, Tyentegen, was well liked in the tribe. He was a remarkable storyteller, and he knew all the old legends of the tribe. He was also a poet and a minstrel, singing the stories of the Beavers of old; even beyond the limits of Komaxala's rule, his songs were known and repeated. His face was wrinkled and old, but his eyes were gentle, looking out timidly from the downcast expression of his face.

"*Hua!*" he muttered; and in the Beaver tongue he said: "My old woman walks too fast. I cannot keep up with her . . . my legs are as weak as those of a newborn deer."

Several of the young men made laughing replies to this, with pointed references to the legs of Tyentegen's mate, which were big enough to support the body of a moose. Tyentegen, shaking his head and sighing, passed the gamblers and, with what seemed a last expenditure of strength, tottered toward the hut into which Sagafewah had peered.

"Shut up with your blabbering!" Sagafewah screeched from her massive repose on the ground. "Get some food cooked—get things in order!"

Dan stared in wonderment at this queer reversal of the accepted Indian relations between husband and wife. The old woman struggled slowly to her feet and waddled toward her spouse, still screaming imprecations. The young men at the gambling game laughed and shouted at her, but she paid no attention to them.

Dan heard a further commotion, and saw a number of women filing into the village. They were loaded with burdens, and children were galloping among them, and in a few cases small children rode on top of the burdens the women carried. Some children were crying; others were screaming and shouting. The entire village was suddenly filled with confusion. The harsh voices of women mingled with the discordant cries of their offspring as they called to each other and scolded their children.

The men at the gambling circle paid little attention to the new arrivals, scarcely raising their heads to take notice of the confused entry of the women of the tribe. Dan was impressed, and he was particularly impressed by one woman who was younger than most. She arrived with three other women, who seemed to have kept apart from the main body of the Indian wives. She moved swiftly and gracefully, her slim body gliding quickly across the ground as if her feet hardly touched the earth! All four of the women in the detached group were carrying burdens, and they stopped some distance away from the others and set their burdens on the ground. None of the women spoke to them, nor did they speak to anyone else.

Dan looked in open admiration at the one who had first caught his glance. She seemed taller than the rest, and held her body with the poise of a deer arrested for an instant in flight through the forest. She was dark, and her hair was long and black; her eyes, large and dark, flashed as she looked around, but she never seemed to look at any one person.

A stately woman stepped from the largest of the tents—the tent of Komaxala—and walked toward the other women. This was Bedodid, the wife of Komaxala. She walked toward the four women and, with swift gestures that revealed both dignity and authority in every movement, pointed to the tents where each woman was to go. Three of the women picked up their burdens and without a word walked toward the tents Bedodid had indicated. The fourth—the tall girl Dan had observed with special interest—remained standing with Bedodid for a moment.

The chief's wife spoke to her, made a few signals with her hands, and then stooped and picked up part of the girl's burden. The girl put the rest of the bundle on her head, and followed Bedodid toward the big hut of Komaxala.

Dan watched this with great interest. He decided that the tall girl, with the dark hair and flashing eyes, must be someone of importance, to be taken into the tent of the chief of the tribe. He wondered why the others were treated differently—and why the four women were given this special reception.

While Dan was pondering these things, Komaxala stepped from his hut and walked toward Dan. He held one hand upraised, as a sign of invitation.

"The son of the black spirit will be the guest of Komaxala," the chief said, in measured words.

Dan followed Komaxala into the hut and immediately saw the tall girl at the far side. She sat apart from the rest, looking at no one.

"Who is she?" Dan asked Komaxala, pointing to the girl.

The chief did not reply. Dan then turned to the girl and asked, "What is your name?"

He spoke the words in Beaver; he had learned this among other simple expressions. But the girl did not reply or even look at him. For an instant she seemed frightened; then her features resumed their composure. Her features were well modeled, with a strong nose; and her large, luminous eyes gave an expression of character which Dan had never before seen on the face of a woman.

Komaxala turned to him.

"Black man, you have spoken to an unfortunate person. You do not know the traditions of our people, but this woman is our daughter. She may not speak to anyone or be spoken to. Her name is Thela, and she is unclean and cannot be regarded as a part of our tribe until at least the next two moons have disappeared. Her husband was killed in a fight in which men of our tribe fought with each other. He was my son-in-law and it is possible he was struck by a spear because of her faults, which were known to the spirits. Very often this is the cause of a brave man's death . . . it is impossible to know. Nevertheless, this is the rule of the tribe, and for the next two moons my unhappy daughter must be left alone."

This speech surprised Dan; but it in no way diminished his interest and curiosity. He continued to stare at her with undisguised admiration.

When the evening meal was served, Thela ate from a separate pot of food, cooked over a separate fire. Bedodid carried the meat from the pot on a pointed stick, and handed it to her daughter in such a way that there was no contact between them. Later she thrust the stick in the fire, burning it so that no one else could use it.

Dan learned from the words of the chief that Bedodid had given birth to four children: three sons and the daughter, Thela. She was a woman of strange powers. Once many years ago she had received a warning from the spirits that the Crees were about to attack the Beavers, and her words had enabled the Beavers to prepare an ambush and thus escape a disastrous defeat. Those of the tribe who had refused to be guided by the premonition of a woman and were not prepared for the attack had been forced to flee and had ended in starvation and misery.

Dan looked at the tall, stately woman with great interest. She was indeed the mate of a chief. Her words were never spoken with arrogance or anger, but they had a certain dignity; and her authority among the women of the tribe was never questioned. His glance shifted to Thela, and he saw in her the same qualities . . . She would be a wife fit for a chief.

After the members of the chief's household had eaten, Dan searched in his bag for some tobacco. He passed this around to each person. Some of the elder warriors, who had eaten in the hut of the chief, silently took the piece and sliced off some shavings.

Dan then passed the tobacco to the woman, who took smaller shavings of tobacco. The piece was returned to him without being offered to Thela.

"Yo' daughter don' smoke?" Dan asked in English.

Komaxala understood the meaning of his words, and he turned to the colored man and said gravely:

"I have explained to my guest the customs of our people. Only her mother may offer her anything. Time must pass before her uncleanness will disappear. If there is a child of her husband in her belly, this will take away the evil that she may have done. If there is no child, the wise men of the tribe will have to decide how many moons must pass before she can be approached by anyone except her mother."

Dan listened to the chief, but in his mind was only one thought: This would offer an opportunity to explain to these people how great was the power of God, and how much mercy Jesus had for His children.

"Yo' is talkin' about the Devil—not about God," he said, with sudden importance. "God don' let any of His child'en suffer."

He fished in his bag for another piece of tobacco, and handed it to Bedodid. She lifted a hand, indicating that they had taken all that custom permitted. Dan pointed to the girl.

Komaxala lifted his hand this time, his face becoming stern; but Dan paid no attention to this. When Bedodid refused the second time to take the tobacco, he rose and carved enough shavings for a pipeful. Then he walked over to the girl and handed the tobacco to her.

Komaxala also stood up. He stepped across the room and snatched the tobacco from Dan's hands and flung it through the opening of the hut.

Dan looked at the chief's blazing eyes; suddenly he sat down, saying nothing. He had been about to make a talk on the importance and power of his God, who was the strongest of all spirits; but Komaxala's action, and the anger in his eyes, put an end to that idea.

"Black man," the chief said, "this house is located in the land of the Beavers. Everyone who comes into this place must follow the rules of our tribe. No woman whose husband has been newly killed will be allowed to extend her misfortune to others of the tribe. This is a rule that will be followed by all who live in this place, and by those who visit this place."

He sat down, and Dan also sat quietly, saying nothing for some time. It was in his mind that at the next opportunity he would show with his rifle which God was the most important —the spirit of the Beaver Indians or the God of the white folks and colored folks, which the Reverend Sam had talked about down in Georgia. He knew which God would triumph in such a test, and his thick lips parted in a smile.

The next morning the camp stirred very early. The women were at work fishing when the braves began to come out of their huts. Dan followed Komaxala as he strode from place to place, observing the work. In Dan's mind there was only one thought: When it came time to hunt, he would show these believers in many spirits how the real God could direct a man's aim with a rifle! The memory of the events of the night before did not sit very pleasantly in Dan's thoughts. He had inteɪded to deliver a homily on the power and mercy of God, but in some way Komaxala had stopped him. But Dan knew how the Indians admired a great hunter; and there was no hunter in all the North greater than Daniel Williams!

Komaxala walked down to the lake where the women were fishing, and the braves were making up the casks for *klina*. They were formed of birchbark pieces made watertight with resin and supported by mounds of earth and spruce branches. Here the fish would be cooked down into *klina*, the fish oil used in tanning animal hides and for lamp fuel, and stored in *klina* casks for winter trapping.

Komaxala suddenly took Dan by the arm and pointed into the forest.

"Black friend, do you see the warningbird?"

Dan did not see the bird at first, nor did he know what it was. But his natural keenness as a hunter made him quickly spot the bird to which Komaxala pointed.

"The warningbird sits all day on the top of a bare tree or pole, and if something moves, the bird immediately flies to it," Komaxala said. "The hunter knows this, and will follow the warningbird to a moose or caribou. Two men will be enough." He turned and signaled to one or two braves, who also had observed the bird, that he and the black hunter would follow the bird.

"Come!" he said to Dan, and started into the forest. Dan followed quickly. Komaxala carried only a spear, but he turned his eyes appraisingly toward Dan's rifle. Wapahu and his two companions had told him much of the black man's prowess with a gun.

The blows of axes and other sounds of the men working with the fish scaffold and *klina* casks faded into the silence of the forest. The warningbird, observing the movements of the two men through the trees, returned several times to them, but each time swerved and darted into the deep recesses of the forest. Komaxala indicated by signs to Dan that there was a big animal close by: perhaps a moose or a bear. Bears were often too stupid to be frightened by noises, but a moose would move quickly at the sound of their approach. The Indian walked silently, but Dan pushed through bushes and thickets with less caution.

Each time the warningbird returned, Dan was able to spot it. He felt a strange excitement growing within him. This was a new kind of hunting, and his inner sense of delight at stalking hidden prey took possession of him; he grinned as he walked, and at times could hardly restrain himself from laughing.

Komaxala made a quick signal with his hand. Dan was afraid he might misunderstand the meaning of such signals, and he stopped. He dared not shout to Komaxala for fear the sound would frighten away the game. So he followed as rapidly as he could, as Komaxala moved forward again.

Komaxala slid into the grass on his stomach, all but concealed from Dan's sight. Dan did not know the Indian art of crawling like a snake through the grass, scarcely disturbing it. He got down on his knees, thrusting his rifle ahead of him. The sharp thorns and brambles cut his skin, and he found it was difficult to move along the ground.

Komaxala had long ago spotted the animal that the warningbird had seen, and when Dan came close to him he could see a moose some distance away. The moose is the largest animal in the woods, but it has learned to hide itself in the masses of branches. Standing close to a tree, its antlers look like a part of the forest. A hunter, not used to using his eyes in the forest, may walk very close to a moose without seeing it.

But Komaxala knew the animals of the woods. He knew the moose was not looking toward him; therefore its attention was attracted elsewhere. Since the moose remained standing in one place, it must see a large animal. Komaxala knew at once that the moose had detected a grizzly bear.

The grizzly is the most unpredictable animal in the forest. It may lie in wait to attack its prey, or stalk it. It can be well-fed and uninterested, or it can be hungry and savage. There are many tales of grizzlies among the Indians; old Kavli, who lived to be more than a hundred years old, told of grizzlies that carried away young girls and first raped them and then destroyed them.

Komaxala moved forward slowly, his spear held in his hand. Its point was sharp and it had tasted the blood of other grizzlies. The chief crawled cautiously through the grass until suddenly his eyes caught the movement of the bear against the yellow grass.

The bear had seen the moose, but seemed to have no desire to fight. It had moved into a patch of red berries and was nibbling at these, when suddenly it turned and in a single bound cleared a fallen tree trunk. The grizzly evidently intended to settle the issue with the moose, which stood watching it.

The jump put the bear on the flank of the moose. It also brought it to within a few feet of Komaxala, who had not expected this diversion. The eyesight of a bear is not good, but it was close enough to see the two black eyes of the Indian hunter, staring through the grass. And the man-scent, which the bear hates, drew its attention from the moose.

Komaxala was not entirely prepared for the attack. He had been watching the moose as he moved forward, and had forgotten to keep his eyes on every movement of the bear. He managed to squirm around quickly, facing the bear. His knife was pinned in the sheath under his body, and he had only the spear to meet the attack.

Had Komaxala been upright in the grass, he could have met the charge with his spear poised and perhaps inflicted such a deadly thrust that the bear would have retreated or been killed by the goring of the spear. But he had been stalking a moose, and was not ready to change to the proper way of meeting a bear.

The dark mass of the bear loomed in the grass above him, and in an instant the sharp claws of the bear came down in a sweeping arc. Komaxala tried to roll over, thrusting his spear upward to meet the charge. But it was the side of the spear, not the point; and the great cloud of fur, with its reeking stench and hot breath seemed to collapse over him.

It was some time before Komaxala opened his eyes. He heard the sound of a voice, and then he saw some light. The massive animal was being rolled off him. In the light above he saw the black face of a man, his heavy mouth open, giving vent to a rumbling laugh.

Dan had been some distance behind the Beaver chief when the bear sprang at him, but his shot had caught the bear in the face as it completed its charge. The last dying sweep of its claws had raked the Indian's back, and Komaxala's body was already bathed in blood.

Dan was busy wrapping the wounds with strips of his shirt, which he had torn up to make bandages. Komaxala's brain was afire with pain, but he lifted his hand to indicate to Dan that he should do nothing further. The chief needed to know where he had been hurt, and how badly. His side had been smashed by the impact of the dying bear's body, and every time he breathed intense pain shot through his body. But Komaxala was a Beaver, and he was able to stand pain without so much as betraying it in his face.

Finally Komaxala gasped, "A bear was killed by your shot." The words were spoken as casually as possible; Komaxala tried not to appear impressed by what had happened.

Dan, however, had no such reticence. He grinned eagerly,

126

and suddenly his great laugh boomed out. It was not possible for him to suppress it.

"Dan sho' done shot straight," he said, still grinning. "That bear got his jaws open to bite yo' and Dan jes hit him smack in the throat."

Dan's bullet had gone through the brain of the big grizzly. He had shot from a distance of perhaps a hundred and fifty yards, and the bullet had struck the only place that could have killed the bear instantly. Komaxala knew this, but he had no desire to make any unnecessary admissions. He looked over and saw the big colored man on his knees.

"Sweet Jesus, Yo' done made Dan shoot straight again," Dan was muttering, his hands clasped in front of him and his large head thrown back so that his eyes were staring upward. "Dear Jesus, maybe Yo' will help Dan make these red folks to be baptize in the glory of the Lord, Amen!"

This was one of the most compact prayers Dan had ever said, and he was proud of it. He leaned back and laughed in such a way that even Komaxala, in the agony of his pain, stared at the black man in wonder.

Finally Komaxala said, between his clenched teeth:

"You will have to skin the bear, black friend. I cannot help you!"

Dan looked down at the hurt Indian, and grinned again. He pulled Komaxala's knife from its leather sheath, and began to skin the bear. Dan pointed almost gleefully to the hole in the skull where his bullet had gone through.

"Look at this here hole!" he exclaimed. "Right smack in one side an' out the other! Sweet Jesus sho' made Dan shoot straight!"

Dan was about to continue his exploitation of the religious significance of what had happened, but he looked down and saw that Komaxala had closed his eyes. The Beaver chief apparently was not in the mood to engage in any further religious discussion.

By the time Dan had cut away the hind quarters of the bear, Komaxala opened his eyes again.

"It would be good if you would cut off the head and place the skull beside me," he said, in the Beaver tongue. "In a moment I will help you . . . but now the spirit of the bear must be reconciled. This is an honor for the bear that you must give him . . ."

Dan looked down at the chief again. Something in those black eyes, glinting from the iron mask that had settled upon the features of the pain-racked Indian chief, stopped him from disputing the request.

"Dan cut off the head," he muttered. And with these words he began to saw at the thick muscles that protected the neck of the huge grizzly, hacking away at the head which he finally dismembered and rolled over beside the fallen Indian chief.

CHAPTER ELEVEN

The sun was falling behind the trees, and long shadows made the earth feel cool. Dan looked at Komaxala, lying helpless on the cold ground, and tried to decide whether it would be better to wait for other Indians to come or to try to carry the wounded chief back to the village.

"This ground's too cold for yo' cuts," he finally told the Indian. "Dan is strong enough to carry yo'."

The Indian shook his head.

"First make fire," he said. "Fire scare animals away from meat. Make fire on other side of bear." He indicated by a gesture that the smoke would blow across the bear meat. "Smoke meat not good for wolves and foxes."

Dan understood. He built a big fire. After it was burning fiercely he applied himself to the task of hoisting the chief up on his shoulders. Dan knew the Indian must be suffering great pain; but Komaxala said nothing, not even a groan escaping his compressed lips.

Dan also knew that if the situation were reversed, he would be groaning and perhaps yelling in agony at every twist of his shattered side. This annoyed him slightly; it seemed to give the Indian a certain edge over him in human strength and endurance. As usual, Dan referred this vague contest to his heavenly sponsor, wondering if God would understand if Dan should give the Indian just a small twist to make him yell out in pain. He decided that this would not be understood; and there was no time to address a prayer to God, explaining that it would be in the interests of converting these red heathen to make the chief yell ever so slightly.

While Dan was thinking about this, he was also lifting the Indian as gently as possible to his massive shoulders. When Komaxala was finally mounted on his shoulders, with his legs caught fast in the grip of Dan's powerful arms, the queerly assorted pair started back through the forest toward the Beaver village.

Dan plodded forward, the Indian directing him by touching his shoulder. He walked carefully with his burden; several times Dan was on the point of setting Komaxala down so that he could rest; but he knew that he could never get the wounded chief back on his shoulders again, so he kept on. When they were a short distance from the camp Dan let out a shout.

"Hello! I got yo' chief—right here! Dan got him!" The Indians came out to meet them. There was neither surprise nor alarm on their faces as they helped Komaxala down from Dan's shoulders. They quickly put together a stretcher made of barked spruce poles, cleverly laced with branches and twigs. Komaxala was carried on this stretcher to his hut.

Dan stumbled after them, and finally threw himself down on the grass, unable to move. For some time none of the Beaver braves spoke to him or even appeared to notice him. Meanwhile signs passed between Komaxala and the other braves; the chief evidently wished all to understand that the black visitor in their village had killed the bear that attacked Komaxala, and had then brought the chief back to his people.

This was a matter of more than passing importance. Regardless of what happened in the future, one fact would always remain: Komaxala, the chief of the Beavers, now owed his life to the "son of the black spirit."

Dan hardly understood the significance of this at the moment. He was too tired to think, and he sat for some time outside the hut of Komaxala, trying to recover his shattered strength and vaguely observing the passage of people in and out of the tent. He noticed the rolling figure of Sagafewah—who was known as a great healer among the Beavers—as she waddled into the hut of the chief to take charge. Bedodid, calm and serene as always, spoke to the fat woman as she entered, with an air of gracious authority. Later Ikta came out and spoke to Gnanisk and Kichsibu, directing them to the location of the dead bear.

Dan overheard this, and struggled to his feet. He immediately began to explain to the two young braves how to find the place.

". . . You see big lake, you go right. Behind the lake you see big trees." He used his hands to illustrate, interchanging Beaver and English words. "You keep walking until you find a small stream."

By this time the two boys were showing some impatience. Finally Ikta walked over to the boys.

"Our black guest uses many words when one sign will tell the story," he said. Then, with a wave of his hand, he indicated to the boys that they should be on their way. Turning to Dan, he permitted his cold, deep-set eyes to inspect the black man slowly, and his thin mouth twisted slightly.

"What's the matter?" Dan asked. "Yo' don' want me to tell these boys where to find the bear?"

Ikta's bronze shoulders, showing through the skin the fibers of tireless muscles, lifted in a shrug that was more eloquent than his lips. Dan looked into the Indian's black eyes and saw the deadly hatred in them; but since this was something he did not understand, he ignored it.

"Does our black guest really think he can make tracks in the forest that an Indian boy cannot follow?" Ikta said, and turned again to the boys, who had paused to look curiously at Dan, since this was the closest they had come to the black stranger. A flick of his hand and the boys were off, jogging through the trees.

Dan sat alone again.

Soon Bedodid came out of the chief's hut and walked toward him. Her dignity remained unshaken. She had just seen the open wounds on her husband's back and side, where the claws of the bear raked furrows of flesh across the bones of his body. His side was oddly misshapen, where several ribs were cracked or splintered by the power of the bear's sweeping blow. She had merely looked at these wounds while Sagafewah dressed them with leaves and herbs; to have showed more concern would have indicated a lack of confidence in Komaxala's ability to survive any injuries.

Now she looked at Dan, sitting with his sore feet drawn up under him, so that his immense body seemed to be compressed into a single mound of flesh. She extended her hand, almost as if in benediction; and Dan, with a flash of his white teeth, said:

"It's purty lucky Dan's gun shoot straight! I sho' killed that ol' bear!"

A slight frown traced itself on Bedodid's candid face, but it passed almost as soon as it appeared. She smiled gravely and with a single wave of her hand indicated that Dan was permitted to enter the hut. This was an honor no stranger normally would have enjoyed; but the black guest of Komaxala was now more than a guest: he was the savior of the chief of the Beaver tribe.

Dan rose with some effort, wagging his big head, and turned toward the hut. Inside were the old medicine man, Ikta, and Sagafewah, who waddled around the hut with great importance and a kind of massive firmness that brooked no interference with her efforts.

Komaxala lay on the green-thatched stretcher. Across the hut, sitting alone, was the dark-haired girl, Thela. Dan walked over and stood beside her. In the recesses of his thoughts was a vague anger that no one had thought to express in words their gratitude and appreciation for what he had done. He felt that this perhaps was the moment to assert his place in all these activities. Without the aid of his rifle, which had the blessing of Almighty God, there would have been no chief here for them to attend!

He turned to Thela and said:

"Don' yo' help take care of your ol' man?"

Bedodid said, with quiet restraint:

"My daughter does not touch anything . . . at this time."

Dan hunched his shoulders and said, with a touch of defiance in his tone:

"Maybe yo' daughter can help me, then. Dan got some stuff to lay out an' dry . . . an' clothes to mend!" He extended one big hand to the girl.

"Come on!"

Thela looked at him, and then rose to her feet, still not speaking. To cover up the suddenness of his statement, Dan reached in his pocket for a piece of tobacco and handed it to her. The face of Bedodid did not change; she merely watched her daughter take the tobacco and place it in her bag. Then Dan walked out of the tent and the Indian girl followed him. Ikta, crouching beside the chief, stared at Dan. He said nothing, but there was hatred in his eyes.

Komaxala's face glistened like worn leather. He watched Dan but did not indicate by word or sign what was in his thoughts.

Dan had not entertained any notion of doing this when he stepped into the hut. His action was purely spontaneous, aroused by resentment of the apparent nonrecognition of his achievements. He thought in a vague way that this would remind the Indian braves that he had the right to do as he wished: he had saved the life of their chief!

Nevertheless, he was surprised when Bedodid made no sign to detain her daughter. As he strode down toward the place where he had left his store of supplies, including the rather bedraggled tea and the battered teakettle, he saw a rabbit dart across the path.

Dan had picked up his gun when he left Komaxala's hut, and now he raised it to aim at the rabbit. It was a small amount of meat, compared with the big bear he had killed, but somehow Dan felt that shooting the rabbit might impress Thela.

The girl reached out and touched his arm. She pointed to a lynx not far from the rabbit. Her quick eyes had seen this animal stalking the rabbit; without hesitation Dan aimed at the lynx and fired.

By not so much as a glance did the girl betray any surprise at Dan's shot. She walked over to the lynx lying across the branch of a dead tree, and picked up the animal.

Dan followed her. He thought momentarily of getting down on his knees and thanking God for the straightness of his shot, as he often did; but the result seemed so small that it would scarcely be worth praying about. Thela was now walking toward the place where his belongings had been heaped, carrying the dead lynx; she would not even see Dan in prayer.

Dan strode angrily after the girl. By the time he reached the place where his possessions lay, she was already at work straightening out his belongings, laying out his clothes for repairs, and examining the small amount of food left in his knapsack, to determine whether it was worth keeping.

Meanwhile the two boys, who had followed the course of Dan's labored journey through the woods, found the remains of the bear; and Gnanisk, who was the faster runner of the two, returned ahead of Kichsibu with the huge head of the bear.

Dan was in the hut of Komaxala, hunched on the ground near the chief, when Gnanisk entered the hut and rolled the big, bloody head over to the place where the injured chief lay.

Komaxala said nothing, merely looking at the boy; and Gnanisk knew from the glance that he had done well. Dan, however, knew little of these niceties of understanding; he looked at Gnanisk from under his heavy-lidded eyes and said:

"Where the meat?"

Gnanisk lifted his shoulders proudly.

"The meat has been piled up. Women will bring it to the village."

The head of the bear had been brought back as an honor to the bear, and also a tribute to the honor and dignity of Komaxala, who thus showed his perception of the courtesies due the slain bear. To discuss the bear's head, which would be prepared specially with the brains brewed in the skull itself and apportioned carefully among the braves of the Beaver tribe, in the same breath with carrying meat, which was a woman's work, was unthinkable to a Beaver warrior.

Komaxala turned to Dan, his eyes showing both patience and intelligence in spite of the pain that racked his body.

"It is with gratitude that I have received the head of this bear," he said, in the Beaver tongue. Dan understood only a few of the words, but from Komaxala's gestures he understood the meaning. "You will honor my house by eating from the skull, once the food from the bear's head has been prepared."

Bedodid had already set about preparing the bear's head. She drew the brain out through a hole in the back of the skull. This would be brewed in the skull, with secret ingredients, and would give to the men who ate it the courage and strength of the bear; in the case of Komaxala and his black guest, it would strengthen their friendship with the bonds of the common knowledge of the manner in which the bear was killed.

This was understood by every member of the Beaver tribe; but Dan had had no previous experience in this sort of thing, and he merely said to Komaxala:

"Ef'n you got no use for the hide, I can use it, all right. My blanket is full of holes and almost wore out."

Komaxala nodded. After Bedodid had prepared the brain, mixing with it roots which had great medicinal power and strong leaves from spicy trees, and cooking it in the skull itself, Dan and Komaxala ate from the preparation.

While they were eating, Thela came quietly into the tent and took her usual place at the far side. Dan looked at her, and his mind was again filled with a great resentment. He had lost out each time in his exchanges with Komaxala, even when he should have been accorded the respect and gratitude due a man who had saved the life of the chief. Because of this, and with obstinate nonconformity, he poured part of his share of the concoction from the bear's head into an earthen bowl and handed it to Thela.

The girl took the bowl, but looked at her father, without touching what was in it. This was perhaps the first time in the history of the Beaver tribe that a woman had been offered food that was so beneficial to warriors—the brain of the bear, man's most dangerous enemy in the forests! Never before had a warrior so abased himself that he permitted the question of a woman's wishes even to disturb talk between men on such a sacred occasion. The brain had been prepared by the wife of the chief, who had endured the greatest of privations with her husband; yet she would never touch the preparation of bear brain. Old Ikta had pronounced it a fit meal for the strengthening of friendship between Komaxala and the black visitor, and it was for men, not women.

And now a woman—and an unclean one at that—was offered a part of this feast!

On the other hand, if Komaxala refused Dan the right to give part of his food to Thela, it might cause the black visitor to believe that the Beavers thought more of food than of their honor; that they worshipped food as weak people do who disgrace themselves in times of hunger.

Komaxala looked at Dan. He had showed himself different from other men. He was not only a man of enormous size and strength, and certainly of unusual color; but he could shoot with an ability to hit what he aimed at that far surpassed anything ever seen by a Beaver brave.

Komaxala gave no sign of either anger or disappointment.

"Men eat everything," he said, by way of gracious acceptance of the situation. "They eat bear meat, and also the meat of cats, dogs, snakes, and frogs. Only women distinguish between what is good to taste and what is not good." He spoke in Beaver, and left it at that; and since Dan did not understand what he said, he merely grinned with satisfaction when Thela ate silently from the dish, acting as if she merely obeyed the wishes of a man whom she must please as a guest in her father's house.

Unaware of the devastation that had been wrought in ancient traditions of the Beavers, Dan continued to express his satisfaction with all that had happened. Komaxala listened courteously, as Dan again and again told the story of how he killed the bear.

The rest of the bear meat had been brought back by women who had followed Gnanisk and Kichsibu to the place where the bear was killed, and by now all the tribe was feasting. Komaxala found himself so strengthened by the concoction of bear brain and herbs that he was able to move out and sit by the fire and shout to the other braves, in spite of his wounds.

The three "unclean" women whose husbands, like the husband of Thela, had been killed in the fight with Attalu and his followers, had no right to take part in this common feast. They sat apart from the rest, eating only what was brought to them by Bedodid.

Dan watched this, and decided that it was time to push forward his rather hazy notion of converting the Beavers to a better understanding of the power and importance of God. His first thought had been that when the feast was ended, he would bring out his Bible and preach to them, much as the Reverend Sam had preached after a barbecue in the old days down in Georgia.

But now as the feast continued and the dances began before the fires, he observed a young Indian girl standing a little distance away from the rest. She seemed to hesitate as if she were uncertain where to go; and then Dan noticed that she wore a blindfold.

Dan watched for a time, and saw other women join the girl and lead her toward the outer ring of tents in the village. Suddenly Dan rose. It was in his mind that there was something sinister in this, perhaps something cruel. He followed the girl and her guides as they descended along a trail toward the lake.

Dan began to run, shouting through the stillness of the night:

"*Tes-kwa! Tes-kwa!* Stop! Stop!"

The women began to shout, too; and the blindfolded girl started to run, stumbling through the underbrush. The other women caught up with her and gathered around, while Dan lumbered up, still shouting for them to stop.

Suddenly he saw Bedodid standing among the women. She stepped forward with an expression of calmness on her face.

"*Sask-atch, muni!*" she said quietly. Dan understood the words; they meant "Go away, stranger!"

He stopped, suddenly realizing that he had come upon something that was for women alone. The girl was named Lalaska, and as it happened, she had reached a state of physical development that is regarded among all people—Indians as well as others—as being the passage from girlhood into womanhood.

"Lalaska must go to a hut where she will be alone," Bedodid said, still speaking quietly to Dan, so that none of the other women could hear her words. "Your heart is good, black friend of my husband, but your mind lacks understanding of our customs."

Dan turned and walked back toward the village. He was ashamed; and more than that, he was annoyed at Jesus for having let him fall into such a trap.

It was some days later he learned that one of the young braves—Gnanisk, the young Beaver who had returned with the bear's head, and who was little more than a boy—had also followed the trail to the hut where Lalaska had been taken into her seclusion. Gnanisk had gone for reasons other than a desire to rescue her, however. He had remained for many hours near the hut, hoping to see what transpired; and he had finally climbed a tree to get a better view.

It was while he was in the tree, sitting between the joint of a dead branch and the trunk of the tree, that his hold gave way and he plunged to the ground. It was easy to see what had happened, from the signs on the ground. He had fallen upon a porcupine, and the sharp quills of the animal had been driven into his face and arms and the upper part of his body.

How long Gnanisk remained there was not known, even to him. He lost consciousness, blinded with the pain of the sharp quills, some of which pierced his eyes, pinning the eyelids shut. The pain and blindness overcame him and he lay on the wet ground for hours while the Beaver braves searched farther into the forest for him.

When the dogs of the village found Gnanisk, he was more dead than alive. Lalaska had already been brought back to the village when the torn and bleeding body of the young brave was carried in. Komaxala, who had given the order to search for Gnanisk, now had to make a decision as chief: whether to let the boy die in the agony of his shameful action or whether to kill him, thus sparing him the torture of a slower death.

Dan was sitting near Komaxala's hut, laboriously mending the tattered pages of his Bible, when the boy was brought into the village and laid on the ground in front of the chief's house. His eyes were bleeding from the wounds of the porcupine quills. Even though he lived, it was evident he would never see again.

Sagafewah, who was always consulted on matters of this sort, looked at the boy's bloody face and wagged her head. She assisted in extracting the quills that remained in Gnanisk's flesh, but she offered no hope for his survival.

The fat wife of Tyentegen made her views clear, in a strident voice: Since Gnanisk had violated the rules of the tribe in such a shameful fashion, it would be pointless to try to heal his wounds. And since he would never have the use of his eyes, he would always be useless to the tribe. Sagafewah, to illustrate this point, lifted one eyelid which had been nailed to

138

the eyeball with the needlelike points of the porcupine quills.

The sight of the bloody socket filled Dan with horror as he watched; and it also aroused in him an urge once more to show them the power and mercy of his God.

Struggling to quell the qualms of his stomach, the black man stepped forward to the side of the stricken boy.

Sagafewah was saying, "This boy has violated the laws, and therefore I cannot help him. It is better to let him die! The Great Spirit is angry, and his life would be an eternal misfortune for our people and a bitter sorrow for his relatives."

What Sagafewah said was highly proper, and conformed with all the customs and beliefs of the Beavers. She looked at Komaxala, who sat propped up on his litter within the hut, observing all that was happening and listening to the words of the old woman.

Dan walked around the boy, who lay only half conscious, his body swimming in pain. He looked in at Komaxala. Then he went into the hut.

"This boy can live," he said—and this time his voice was low, as if he knew he must persuade Komaxala by reason, not by loud speaking. "Jesus, have mercy on Yo' afflicted chil'!" Dan raised a pious hand to the sky, and Komaxala watched him steadily. "Lemme keep this boy, chief, an' I promise he'll get well again!"

Komaxala's expression was grave: neither friendly nor hostile. He was now sitting in judgment on one of his people, and this was the most sacred obligation of a Beaver chief. For some time he spoke with Dan, in a voice that the others could not hear.

It was known that Gnanisk could never see again. And a blind brave was worse than useless, since he could not contribute to hunting or to battle; yet he must be cared for in some way. Komaxala pointed this out to Dan, but the big colored man stuck stubbornly to his request.

When it was decided, Dan walked out and took Sagafewah by the shoulders, thrusting her away from the boy. She screamed, waddling around in circles, glaring first at Dan and then at the other Indians.

Dan crouched down beside the bed of branches and leaves upon which Gnanisk had been laid. In his pocket were some scraps of paper that had been torn from the pages of his Bible when he was trying to repair the damage caused by the bullet.

He took two of these and laid them on the spongy mass of the boy's eyelids. Dan had no idea why he did this: it was an instinctive action, born of his unquestioning faith in the efficacy of prayer and the power of the holy words in the book of God.

Even Ikta forbore to comment on such an action. It was obviously powerful medicine, and he remained silent, knowing he would have to consider this in the solitude of his own hut and determine what measures might be taken to counteract the effect of the black man's magic.

Ikta knew also, without even admitting it to himself, that it would be particularly disconcerting if—after this mysterious application of the bits of the black man's magic paper—Gnanisk were to recover the use of his eyes! Such things had been known to happen; and it was not beyond the realm of possibility that the black man possessed such powerful forces of the great spirits that he could accomplish this sort of miracle.

Ikta was also wise in other ways. If the experiment with Gnanisk failed—if the boy should die—then the black visitor's hold on the imagination of the Beaver people, and even his strange ability to violate rules and still be excused by Komaxala, would vanish with the spark of the boy's life.

So Ikta said nothing. Dan, after his queer ministration, lifted the boy as he would have lifted a child, and carried him to a hut which had been designated for him as long as he remained a guest of the Beavers.

Sagafewah waddled after him, still shouting imprecations and screaming for some kind of support from the Indians who trailed after them. The strange procession wound up at Dan's hut, but when he disappeared with his gruesome load into the interior of the hut, the others wandered off.

Strange things had been wrought since the black man first came to the tribe. Perhaps the strangest of all was that the Beavers consented to give one of their number—maimed and useless as he was—to this stranger, to be possessed by the black man as long as he lived.

Such a thing had never happened before in the memory of the oldest living member of the tribe, even in the memory of Klivi, the ancient crone who had long since passed the century mark and knew of the days when the Crees had hunted the Beavers, driving them across the plains, killing their men, and taking their women for slaves.

CHAPTER TWELVE

During the warm summer days the women fished in the lake and in the streams that ran into the lake, filling the fish scaffolds on the beach. They laughed and chattered and bawled at each other, working steadily while the braves sat under the comforting shade of trees, or played at the gambling game on the grass.

The fish had to be cleaned and split for drying; and other fish were thrown into bark casks to be stewed into *klina*. These included the whole fish, head, guts and all, which then lay rotting, so that the stench and pollution were carried on the wind into the camp and even into the woods for many miles. The *klina* boiling was a special function; no woman who was pregnant or "unclean" because of the untimely death of her husband could take part in this work. Those who were skilled at making *klina* had a special honor; the right to sit closest to the lamps during the winters so that they could perform their sewing and other tasks with plenty of light.

As the summer wore on and the work at the village became

141

better organized, the braves were able to go on long hunting trips. Dan accompanied the hunters on many of these trips, and when his long rifle spoke in the coolness of the forest, it was always with authority. He became a familiar member of the village, although he was never clearly understood by most of the braves because of his peculiar habits and even more peculiar color.

At first Dan spent much of the time in his hut, taking care of the needs of the boy, Gnanisk. There were still bits of quills in the boy's flesh, which festered out slowly, and with much pain. Gnanisk recovered his health slowly, and his sightless eyes seemed to follow Dan with instinctive faith as he moved in and out of the hut.

Once or twice the fat wife of Tyentegen came into Dan's hut, and her shrill voice could be heard abusing the boy; but on each occasion Dan hurried to the hut and shoved her out with as much physical force as was required, which was not inconsiderable.

Once, as he approached the hut, he heard her berating the boy.

"You are blind and will always be blind—no matter what pieces of paper that black fool puts on your eyes," she shouted. "You will be left out some day where you will have no food and you will die slowly—unless you should be lucky enough to have wolves come by and eat you!"

Dan pushed his way into the hut and gripped Sagafewah so quickly that his powerful fingers sank into the fat folds of her shoulder.

"Get out!" he shouted, in his deep voice. "Get out—afore I forget the mercy of sweet Jesus and kick yo' in the ass, like I would kick a mule! Yo' is evil, woman—jes' a damned evil ol' woman!"

Sagafewah screamed and twisted away with surprising agility, and aimed a sweeping blow at Dan,. which he parried almost indifferently. He grabbed her again and shook her violently.

"God has brung the dead to life—an' He can save this boy!"

142

Dan shouted in rumbling tones. "When He has saved this boy, He's gonna show Dan how to build a church to His glory an' convert all yo' damned heathen!"

Sagafewah, having finally squirmed out of the grip of Dan's big hands, lunged through the door, still hurling curses and imprecations over her shoulder. The other Beavers, having accepted Dan's strange conduct—even his nursing of Gnanisk, which was one of the strangest of all his weird acts—laughed as the old woman waddled ponderously across the clearing to her hut. They knew poor Tyentegen would be the ultimate loser; she would aim every insult and blow she reserved for Dan upon the cowering figure of her husband. But old Ikta, watching the scene, turned and looked thoughtfully in the direction of Dan's hut.

The notion had been gradually glimmering in Dan's mind that God intended him to carry the light of Christianity into the heart of these heathen Indians. This glimmer was rapidly becoming a bright flame. His spontaneous and aimless act of kindness toward Gnanisk—which actually arose from resentment against the failure of the Beavers to recognize his prowess rather than a conscious act of mercy—was developing into a small crusade, the seed of a flowering campaign of enlightenment in one of God's more primitive orchards on earth.

Dan knew that no one else in the village—not even the boy's mother—would have cared for Gnanisk as he had. Therefore, he fervently hoped for a "miracle." If God intended this to be a demonstration of His powers, perhaps He would restore the boy's sight—thus giving to Dan the full credit and reputation of having produced the miracle.

But even if God should not wish to carry the thing that far —and Dan knew from previous experience that God did not always take advantage of the opportunities Dan offered Him for showing His powers—nevertheless, Gnanisk would always prove a useful helper. He could keep Dan's hut in order, and learn to prepare food and even run errands. Daniel Williams —a one-time poor black boy in the slave days of Georgia— would be the possessor of a servant of his own!

Dan liked to walk through the woods, and he learned to follow the hunters tirelessly, and even quietly. The Indians were faster and moved more silently, but Dan could outlast any of them in long journeys through the forest. And his unerring rifle quickly made up for any gaps in distance that might favor the Indians, with their poor guns and even poorer ability to use them.

When Dan saw game, he walked straight toward it. He had learned to move through the forest without stirring the branches or stumbling over stones, but he seldom was able to use the caution of the Indians. Yet the results were always in his favor; it was he who got the big game!

The buying power of Indians in the trading posts of the white men depended entirely on the number of beaver and fox skins they brought in. The white traders never seemed to be satisfied with what they got. There seemed to be more and more white people farther and farther away who wanted these skins, and the Indians knew there would always be a market for their catch.

But the Indians understood that the beavers themselves were not without limit in the number of skins they could provide. Beavers like to stay where they are born, if there are enough trees to cut down; but here in the forest of the Beaver Indians they had begun to move away. The Indians traced their movements to the old beaver ponds far up in the mountains, and knew that they must follow the beaver to these places if they were to get skins.

They set out for these heights late in the summer, reaching them after several days' walking. From here it was easy to see the higher mountains to the west, beyond a great valley carved out of the sharp walls of the western peaks. On the floor of this valley lay numerous lakes, long and narrow and glittering like magnificent blue gems in the soft layer of scrub trees that spread like a great velvet carpet between the dark ridges of the mountains on either side.

Dan had gone ahead of the rest, and had come out through a cleft in the hills, overlooking the great valley. Behind him was the unlucky brave, Kwolsit, who had lost his knife to Ikta in the gambling game. Kwolsit was not young, and was known as a hunter whom the spirits seldom befriended. Whatever he did turned out wrong; and although he was neither stupid nor mean by nature, he was never lucky and so was given all the minor and menial jobs that would have been turned over to women, if there had been any women on the hunt to do the job.

Dan knew that Kwolsit followed him because he was impressed by Dan's great skill as a hunter, and this pleased Dan. He seldom bothered to evaluate the source of admiration or praise directed toward him. It was enough that someone admired him and believed him to be a great man.

He spotted a brown bear down the slope. Without haste he started down the slope to get a clear view of the bear. Kwolsit came behind, light-footed as a wraith. When Dan had a clear view of the bear, he raised his gun effortlessly and fired. The bear, who had probably never been far from this place since he was born—and therefore had no foreknowledge of human hunters or the deadly power of a rifle that spoke from great distances—toppled over on the ground and lay still. Dan's laugh rumbled over the quiet valley like a burst of thunder.

Kwolsit ran back to the others and reported this event, almost as if he had done the shooting himself. Other Indians arrived at the shooting place, and the bear was quickly stripped of its skin, and the hunting party was provided with fresh meat. That night they sat around the fire, each brave broiling a slab of meat on the end of a pointed stick.

Osawask, one of the three young braves who met Dan on his return to Fort St. John, observed that there were no watchers posted; and he spoke to Kwolsit about this. Kwolsit was a much older hunter, but his bad luck had left him without confidence or pride, so he rose and left the fire. No one bothered to toss him a piece of cooked meat to chew on when he sat up on the ridge. He merely walked alone out of the circle of light around the fire, and nothing more was thought about him.

There was so much meat that it would be impossible either to eat it all or carry it. Therefore, it was agreed that the meat should be dried. This meant that they must stay here for a few days, or perhaps two or three would remain to dry the meat. In any event, it was something that could be decided the next day, and one by one the Indians curled up and went to sleep.

Dan remained awake, gazing broodingly into the fire. Each triumph—such as the killing of the bear—should have bolstered his spirits; yet these wonders he was performing brought no response from the Beaver braves, either in gratitude or admiration. They accepted the fruits of his hunting without pleasure or displeasure.

Dan knew that he must perform a real miracle to break through this strange barrier. He bowed his head before the fire, the flickering lights glinting weirdly on the slanted ridges of his temples and his heavy jaws, so that his face looked more like an immense skull than the living face of a man.

Dan began to mutter a kind of prayer, half to himself—although he spoke aloud, since some of the Indians might be partly awake and thus be able to hear him. He looked upward for a moment, where dawn was coloring the sky.

"Jesus, Yo' gotta help Dan pe'form a miracle . . . Yo' jes' gotta! These damn heathen don' know the power an' the mercy of the good Lord, amen!" He paused, and then added, "In Jesus' name I ask it! Amen."

He had just concluded this prayer when a figure drifted silently into the circle of light. It was Kwolsit. His dark, beady eyes shone in the smoldering firelight. He raised one hand and pointed into the west, toward the great valley where the lakes lay.

"Caribou!" he said quietly. He had not spoken loudly, but several of the Indians raised their heads. Kwolsit quickly told his story, his face glowing with pride at the sudden position of importance he had achieved.

He had gone to the top of the ridge, and scanned the country on both sides—ahead of him, and behind. The Beavers were far from their home village, and there was always the possibility that enemies might creep up unsuspectingly in the night

146

and do to the Beavers exactly what the Beavers would have done to the enemy if the situation were reversed.

No one hurried Kwolsit; they realized that he had something of importance to say, and must be given the enjoyment and savor of saying it as he wished.

They all knew this was the time of year when the caribou moved in vast herds, like an immense blanket across a valley. The Indians knew how caribou moved. These strange animals would migrate north early in the spring and return at the end of the summer to a warmer climate; but now and then, if they found an especially fine pasture, their migration might be delayed or diverted.

The cows with their calves would always go farthest north; the bulls would never reach the coast. The Indians understood the reason for this: the cows needed salt more than the bulls. At the end of the warm season they would rejoin each other and head southward in herds so immense that they literally covered the floors of the long valleys that extended from the frozen tundra down to the green slopes of the Rockies west and south of the Peace River.

Kwolsit kept on talking: He had first seen a "warningbird," he said. It flew westward, and then returned; and Kwolsit had climbed to a cliff to observe the bird's progress. In the early dawn, with his sharp eyes, it was possible to see the bird on each return trip. When light began to creep across the hills to the east and spread its painted veil of light over the valley, he saw the caribou.

They were stretched far across the valley, in such a herd that there was hardly a place on the floor of the valley where they could not be seen.

A plan was quickly made among the braves in the camp. A few were to go to the ridge, where Kwolsit saw the caribou, and keep watch of the herd's movements. Dan rose, and picked up his gun. He had not been assigned to this duty, but his actions indicated he was going to be among those who went up to the ridge.

Half of the remaining hunters would be sent back to the

main village. They would have full information, including the geography of the valley, which was important. A great lake extended almost from one side of the valley to the other, with several islands in the middle. It was an effective barrier to the movement of the herd, since it would be necessary for the caribou to swim. Therefore canoes must be brought from the village, so the caribou might be killed in the water as they crossed the lake.

Women would follow the braves in order to scrape skins and dry them as well as carry the meat back to the village. This was the kind of good fortune that did not often happen to the Beavers; and to those who had endured starvation during the frozen winters, it was a sign that the spirits now looked kindly upon the Beaver tribe. Therefore everything must be done properly so that the spirits would know that the Beaver braves had learned how to benefit by such favors.

When Dan reached the top of the cliff he did not see anything at first. But after a while he understood: the brown color he saw on the floor of the valley was not grass or dried-up brush; it was the herd of caribou! He did not know there were so many animals in the world. They floated over the valley like a broad current, moving so slowly—it seemed from that distance—that their progress was barely perceptible. Behind them everything was tramped down. Even the small trees were trampled over. There would be no possibility even of shooting them, except along the edge. How could a hunter get to the animal that was down, and drag it from the herd?

The Indians knew exactly what to do, however. The herd was moving slowly toward the lake at the lower end of the valley, where it was narrower and the mountains rose sharply on either side. There were a few tall trees around the lake; otherwise the land was low and swampy; and the islands in the lake were covered with rich grass.

The leading caribou moved up to the edge of the lake, the foremost being quite cautious about entering the water. Several walked up to the edge, and then turned back. The Indians sat on the cliff, silently watching this. Finally the pressure of animals behind pushed the leaders forward, and they began to move into the lake in order not to be trampled.

They swam to the closest shore, which was one of the large islands. Here there was good grass, and it was obvious that they would cluster on these islands until the sheer numbers of those coming from behind would push them on to the next island.

Behind the caribou herd, following the trailing animals like small yellow scavengers, were coyotes and a few larger gray shapes. These were the wolves. Dan hated wolves. He knew the Indians would regard it as foolish for him to waste ammunition, but, after all, the bullets were his. So he raised his gun and fired. At each shot, a wolf dropped.

When he had fired four or five rounds, Osawask spoke to him, raising his hand.

"Wolves cannot eat enough caribou," he said shortly. "But the talk of guns is not wise at this time. We will go later to the far side of the lake. Here the gun of the black spirit may speak."

Dan rather grudgingly ceased fire. Meanwhile the young braves who had started for the village had arrived at their destination. The first of the braves came running up to Komaxala's tent. It had been a race between them to see which had the greatest speed and the most stamina. Those who arrived first were taken to the chief, nearly fainting from exhaustion. They told him of their discovery.

Komaxala understood quickly that if this hunt should be successful, the tribe would be spared the threat of starvation during the winter. One good caribou hunt was enough to provide food and skins for a year. Many of the skins could be sold to traders; the meat could be dried; life would be luxurious, for their great hunt would be celebrated in many feasts.

Komaxala decided to take part in the hunt personally. His wounds were still far from healed, but he could walk. The making of klina would not be postponed, since it would be an insult to the fish to halt it—and fish oil was needed for the winter. So the women would be divided into two groups: one group to remain at the village, the other to follow the braves to the hunting ground.

Komaxala's gaze fell upon Thela. He called Ikta to his side and spoke a few words to him. The medicine man nodded, his eyes narrowed into tight slits. There was a craftiness in his face which Komaxala, in the excitement of making decisions and issuing orders, possibly did not observe.

"Three moons have passed and my daughter has no child in her belly. It is within the power of the wise men of our tribe to decide whether she is now clean."

Ikta nodded, without speaking.

"It is possible that a leader may be needed in this village— to see all that happens, and direct the women in their work," Komaxala continued.

Ikta nodded again, gravely. This decision was good for him, and both understood this: to have acquiesced in the · early purging of Thela would have gone against the ancient habits of the tribe; but if Komaxala were to take Thela with him, and Ikta remain in the village, he would have no responsibility.

"A warrior needs a canoe so that he may travel on water," Ikta said. "It is well that three moons have passed since this tribe suffered the sorrow of losing many braves."

This was a lie, only two moons had passed. But Komaxala did not challenge it.

"I will have two women carry my canoe to the lake—two women who are not to be taken from the *klina* casks."

"That is well," Ikta said. "We need not take women from the *klina*, which would be bad. We must have oil for the winter. The decision is a wise one."

This also was a lie, and both knew it. The work of the "unclean" women had been only in fishing, and they had not con-·taminated the *klina*. Nevertheless both chose to ignore the deviation from truth and accept what was said, each in his own interest.

Komaxala had to travel slowly because of his wounds; but Thela, who was faster than most braves of the tribe, went

150

swiftly ahead in order to tell the Beaver hunters of the arrival of their chief.

Before she left, the Indian women of the village peeled the bark cover from one of the canoes, so that it was only a skeleton of a boat and light enough to be carried. A mixture of tallow and resin was put into a bag, to seal the seams of the new bark covering, and Thela placed a wide strip of thong across her forehead, attaching the ends to the stripped canoe.

With this burden she set off through the forest. She ran swiftly, and without sleep, for two days, stopping only to snare a rabbit and cook it for nourishment. Her dark body, with its cumbersome burden, moved like a wraith through the trees, and on the second day she slipped out of a fringe of mountain pine and stood among the braves of the tribe who had stayed to watch the caribou.

Thela spoke to no one, since no advance runner had explained the odd decision upon which Ikta and Komaxala had agreed. When the main body of hunters arrived, led by Komaxala, this decision in all probability would be forgotten and Thela would remain in her status as an "unclean" woman— until such time as Ikta decided the ancient taboos were satisfied.

Dan had seen her enter the encampment, and now he approached her.

"Yo' hungry?" he asked.

The girl looked at him directly, her eyes dark with weariness, yet glowing with a fire that never died out. Dan handed her some meat and tallow, which he took from the store of common food; she took it without speaking, and quickly ate it.

Dan always had his cup with him. Even on short trips from the Beaver village he would tie it to his belt. Now he went to the fire and quickly poured some water and a sifting of tea into the cup. After this had boiled a bit, he handed the cup to the girl.

Again she took it without speaking, and drank the tea. Indians understood the great nourishing quality of tea; it restored strength to tired muscles and guarded the body against the spirit of sickness.

After she had drunk the tea, Dan filled a pipe with tobacco and offered it to her. Thela did not look at any other Indians, although many of the braves were watching Dan's actions, but she took the pipe silently and lighted the tobacco from a twig which she took from the fire.

Her own pipe had been buried with her late husband, after it had been smoked to the end, and the ashes poured upon his body. When this was done, Thela had thrown the pipe upon his body as a final honor to him. Since that time, she had had no pipe—because it was against the law of the tribe for anyone to give her one.

Dan observed her as she smoked silently. His heavy lips parted in a grin; but since her face showed neither pleasure nor anger, he stopped grinning and merely stared at her.

The next day the other three taboo women arrived; now there were women to do some of the menial tasks of the hunting camp.

Two canoes were covered with bark and made watertight with resin and tallow, and taken down to the edge of the lake. They would be ready for use when the caribou started swimming from the islands to the shore again. Some of the hunters paddled across to the nearest of the islands to observe the number of caribou at each place. The main body of the herd was either backed up in the valley above the lake or had moved around the lake and was heading southward. But those animals that swam to the islands would remain there until they had eaten all the grass or were pushed off by the arrival of others; and these would furnish the Indians with enough caribou to last for many moons.

The object was to find the places where the caribou would leave the islands, and where they would come ashore. Every precaution had to be taken to be sure that all places were covered.

Meanwhile Komaxala arrived at the camp. He had suffered much from the long trip, but he gave no visible sign of his weakness. His authority was immediately evident. He issued directions, telling each hunter what he must do. He posted watchers at all places, and after a trip around the lake in one of the canoes, he returned and issued orders for moving the camp to a location near the end of the lake where the caribou would come ashore.

Thela, without speaking to anyone, went down to the edge of the lake. She understood her father's directions, and knew someone must scout the exit from the lake. Since no Beaver brave possessed her skill and knowledge, she undertook this task—and she knew she must do it alone.

She pushed a small raft, made of logs, out into the water. Using a long pole to guide the raft, she slowly moved along the shore, staying close to the overhanging trees. If any of the braves saw her, they gave no indication. Who would notice the actions of a woman—and particularly one who was still "unclean"?

The wind had started to rise, making choppy ripples out on the surface of the lake. The older braves looked to the east and noted the small clouds, driven like wisps of smoke across the gray sky. Across the valley there was a faint stirring, like a shiver that struck the trees almost as a breath. At one instant the valley was as quiet as a grave; the next moment the tops of the trees were alive with a steady, whispering ripple of sound.

Thela had cleverly poled her raft close to shore, within the protection of the trees; but a quick gust of wind turned it sideways, and the raft seemed to shoot out on the roughened water of the lake.

She managed to get it on its course again, but now and then the wind would cut through the trees and turn it once more toward the middle of the lake. This happened several times, until it would have been noticed—if any of the braves ashore had deigned to notice such a thing—that each time she turned the raft in its proper direction, she was farther out from shore.

By this time the wind had risen to a screaming gale, and the water on the lake had broken up into choppy waves. Thela

153

had drifted so far out that it was no longer possible to keep close to the shore and make progress, so she turned the raft around and began to pole it directly toward shore.

The reason for this—as any of the Beaver braves would have known—was connected with her taboo. If she set foot on the island—as an "unclean" woman—she would imperil the entire hunt. It might destroy the good luck of the Beaver hunters, and bring starvation to the tribe.

Thela found herself unable to pole the raft against the force of the gale blowing offshore. Suddenly she crouched down and stripped off her leather coat; through the sleeves she thrust two poles and hoisted the coat as a sail so that it would blow her beyond the islands and out into the lake, thus clearing the islands.

The raft swung out into the lake, but suddenly it seemed to have struck a rock or shoal. Dan, who had watched this performance with growing worry, now started down to the shore. He could see the girl, as she struggled to hold the two poles against the rising force of the wind. All at once he lost sight of her, and then he realized there was no one on the raft.

With a shout, he lumbered toward the beach. As he reached the shore, he could see Thela's head, bobbing in the choppy waves. She had either been knocked into the water by the poles or had lost control of them and they had fallen in with her coat. She was swimming toward the coat, which was tangled with the two poles now drifting out into the deeper water of the lake.

The water was icy, and Dan realized that the girl would not have the strength to remain long in that cold water.

None of the other braves had made a move to assist the girl. If the Great Spirit had it in mind to punish her for certain infringements of the code of the tribe, certainly no Beaver brave would risk disfavor by trying to help her. If she were to drown, it would be an obvious act of the spirits of the wind; and there was nothing anyone could do about it.

Dan had no such qualms or inhibitions. He waded into the lake, pulling one of the canoes with him. Even as the cold water rose around his legs, chilling him to the marrow, he found time to mutter a quick appeal to the Lord.

"Jesus!" he said, his voice rising so that it could be heard through the whistling gale. "Yo' gotta help Dan by settlin' down this here lake! Yo' gotta help now, or else Dan mebbe won't be able to do no miracles for Yo'—in the name of Jesus, amen!"

Dan swung one long leg over the edge of the canoe, hauled himself into it, snatched the paddle, and in a few long strokes was able to drive the light craft out into the lake. Some distance ahead he could see Thela; and he kept muttering prayers as he lifted his powerful shoulders to the rhythm of the paddle strokes.

CHAPTER THIRTEEN

Komaxala stood with other Beaver braves, surveying the lake. The rising wind swept the clouds across the heavens until they were massed in a solid, black phalanx advancing against the dying light of the western sky.

The Indian chief observed something that was not according to the behavior of caribou; and he turned in surprise to Osawask and asked:

"Where are the wolves? They do not harry the caribou, and therefore the caribou do not move as we expect them to. Some have even passed on the far side of the lake, against the edge of the mountains, and we have lost sight of them. The wolves should have driven them into the lake."

"Many of the wolves were killed," Osawask replied; Komaxala's face darkened, and his eyes blazed.

"It was foolish to kill the wolves!" he said. "Wolves do not

155

swim! They will not follow the caribou into the lake. They will howl and snap at the feet of the caribou, and drive them into the water to meet us."

Osawask nodded.

"It was the black man who killed them," he said. "He shoots at everything, like a child."

Komaxala said nothing. His eyes, piercing the angry shrouds of the storm, gazed across the lake, but not at Osawask. Finally he said, still without looking at the young brave:

"His ways are strange to us, but he is our guest . . . What he does is to be regarded as right, even when it seems to be otherwise."

Osawask nodded again. At this moment Komaxala saw the raft out on the lake, and his face became taut. He stared through the blackening mists, observing all that happened on the shore and in the water.

No orders had been given for anyone to approach the island in a canoe or a raft. There were no enemies within many days' travel—that much was certain. He saw the bobbing head of Thela, her black hair trailing in the water, and his heart became tight . . . yet he gave no sign of this.

He saw the brown shape of a canoe move out from shore, the huge figure of the black guest hunched forward, driving the paddle deep into the foaming water.

Once again . . . it was the black man.

Meanwhile Dan saw Thela through the haze of water, lashed off the crests of the waves in fine spray by the gale that now blew furiously across the lake. She was a good swimmer, and was able to reach the two floating poles to which her coat was fastened. Resting a hand on the poles, she managed to free her coat from the tangle, when the raft suddenly swung around and slipped off the rocks where it had become caught and drifted away.

The girl was too far from shore to swim back against the fierceness of the wind, so she struck out for the drifting raft.

Dan thrust his paddle in the water with furious strength. He was still some distance away. The water was cold and the rough waves made it almost impossible to swim. He shouted to the girl, but she kept swimming for the raft, and finally he saw the gleam of one dark arm across the logs.

"Jesus, save her . . . save her!" Dan muttered again and again, not knowing why. His lungs were tortured from the driving force of the wind and the exhaustion of paddling. He could see Thela, half submerged, with one arm and now one leg over the edge of the raft. The raft was clearly visible against the water, the waves breaking over it.

His canoe shot toward the raft, but the power of his tremendous strokes, coupled with the force of the wind behind him, sent the canoe past it. He saw the dark face of the girl clearly as the canoe swept by; and a quick glance told him the girl was naked. She had gotten rid of all her clothes so she could swim faster.

Dan dug the paddle deep into the water, trying to check the speed of the canoe. The cold spray lashed into his face as he swung the light craft around and headed back toward the raft.

Cold as the wind was, Dan suddenly was warm inside. The sight of the Indian girl, her dark flesh against the black surface of the raft, awakened a fire in him that was like nothing that had ever happened to him before. He found himself sobbing as he hunched his mighty shoulders against the wind and drove the paddle deeper and deeper into the water.

When he got the bow of the canoe abreast of the raft, he saw that the girl's eyes were closed. Her fingers clung to the round surface of one of the logs and she lay half submerged in the icy waters of the lake.

He reached out and caught her free arm, and pulled her into the canoe. He saw her eyes open, and then she closed them again. Dan jerked off his own coat and wrapped it around her body, covering the bronze smoothness of her frozen skin. While the wind buffeted his canoe, driving it farther out on the lake, Dan knelt down in the boat and carefully tucked the coat around her. When she was safely covered with the coat, lying in the bottom of the canoe, Dan picked up the paddle again.

Now his heart was singing, and unable to contain these feelings, he let loose a triumphant shout as he plunged the paddle into the water with mighty strokes that soon began to drive the boat shoreward against the force of the wind.

Once he stopped paddling and reached down to touch her arm. Her skin was cold and stiff, and her body was motionless; but she had opened her eyes, and he knew that deep in her body was the warmth of life.

Several Indians had come down to the edge of the lake when Dan brought the canoe into shore and beached it. Komaxala stood some distance back, watching Dan lift his daughter from the canoe. Then he came down slowly, hobbling with difficulty. He indicated to Dan that he should carry the girl over to a fire which had been lighted at the base of the cliff, away from the force of the wind.

Bedodid had arrived at the hunting camp with other women just before the storm, and now she came down from Komaxala's hut. She alone could care for the girl, who lay still as death, wrapped in the coat of the black guest.

The wind died down by nightfall, and Komaxala gave the word to the braves that the herd must be watched constantly from this moment on. The sky was still menacing, although it was the light of waning day over the mountains; and the chief knew that if the storm grew worse, the entire herd might be lost during the night. He ordered each hunter to his place.

Dan had watched the girl, Thela, as she was placed beside the fire, and he thought: God has brought this woman to me, and now I will keep her. But he said nothing to Komaxala; now that the danger of the herd's escaping from them had suddenly arisen, all other thoughts vanished from the chief's mind.

Suddenly the sky seemed to open above them. The rain came down in such a torrent that the open fires were soon reduced to smoldering coals, sizzling as the rain washed down upon them. Great peals of thunder shattered the silence of the valley, rolling in steady reverberations from mountain to mountain. Lightning carved white cracks in the sky, and as the storm increased, it became darker until finally daylight was blotted out.

The wind increased in fury, and the grinding noise of broken branches mingled with the rattle of boulders, dislodged from the ground by the water, rolling down the mountainside behind them.

The braves moved under the shelter of the cliff and clung there, waiting for the fury of the storm to spend itself. Dan moved in among them, not far from where Thela lay, partially protected by the overhang of the cliff. He was wet from the soaking he had gotten out on the lake; and now, without the warmth of his coat, he began to feel even colder. He stood helplessly under the cliff, looking out into the inferno of lightning and listening to the crashing noise of thunder and broken branches, and wondering whether the Lord had forgotten him in this hour.

Komaxala's broken ribs and other injuries were forgotten in the storm. The chief stood with his wife closely pressed to his side. Dan could see the glint of the fire, glowing under an overhanging projection of rock; and in the faint light cast by these glowing embers, he could see the shape of Thela, under the black rock of the cliff. Komaxala and Bedodid stood beyond her, so closely held in each other's arms that they looked like a single figure.

Through the drone of the rain and the lash of wind against the trees there came another sound, slowly rising and unmistakable. It was the low, drumming sound of many hoofs; and almost as one, the Indians heard and understood. The herd of caribou had started to stampede.

The lightning and thunder had filled the animals with fear. Those on the islands in the lake huddled together, shelterless against the storm, while those on the shore and across the valley began to move in wild, aimless directions, driven by a rising frenzy and the pressure of other animals around them.

The Indians had set up their camp at the narrow end of the lake, where the caribou would be likely to come out on their way through the valley; but now there was no single place where the caribou might come. In the darkness, lighted by the flashes of fire from the skies, they saw the herd moving senselessly in all directions. The animals were wild with fear, and were aware of nothing around them—trees, or other caribou, or human beings. They forgot which direction they had come from, and many seemed to be circling and heading back toward the mouth of the valley from which they had recently descended.

The Indians, gathering their weapons swiftly, went out into the storm to meet them. They began to kill, but they could not save the animals they killed from the trampling of those thousands of hoofs; and a few could not even save themselves as the caribou tumbled down upon them, pressing from all sides. There were loud screams of hunters, war whoops to terrify and repel the senseless herd.

Dan followed them with his rifle, intending to shoot as many caribou as he could with the bullets in his pocket. In the flashes of lightning he saw himself surrounded by a great sea of horns. They milled and eddied around, stamping upon the sodden ground, made soft by rotting spruce needles. Even though the horns seemed to be perilously close, they did not reach Dan. He stood rigid with fear, feeling a sudden horror of death that swirled around him. He saw the wild, crazed eyes of the animals in the glint of lightning, as they pushed out of a wall of darkness into his vision.

"Oh, Lord!" he roared. And then he looked back across the faint circle of light where Komaxala and Bedodid stood as one against the darkness of the cliff. He knew Thela lay beyond the fire, but she was invisible in the blackness.

The caribou had no leader. Every time one started in a direction, others followed, but they quickly lost sight of the animal they were following and milled around in disorder, leaping into the air and making low, coughing noises. Now and then there was a trembling bellow as one caribou gored another with its horns; and along the shore great splashes could be heard as animal after animal was pushed into the water and struggled to gain footing.

Behind the fire there was a movement, as Thela rose. Apparently recovered from her exhaustion, she had seen the milling caribou, and into her mind must have come the first thought of a hunter: to kill as many caribou as possible.

Dan saw her figure glide past the fire, and he tried to make his way toward her, but she was soon lost in the darkness. At that moment there was a terrific flash of lightning and a crash that sounded as if the heavens had caved in upon them. The noise and shock of flame that split the night stunned Dan for an instant; and when he recovered his senses he caught a glimpse of Thela some distance away, standing above the caribou. The fear-crazed animals seemed to have been stopped for an instant in their swirling movement.

The wind whipped Thela's dark hair away from her face, and in the flash of light from the sky Dan saw her distinctly. She seemed to be standing one instant, and then she started to fall. Dan roared out, and pushed his way into the caribou, heading toward her. A bull caribou hit Dan and nearly knocked him down, but he struggled on, still shouting. Other animals pressed around him, but he pushed forward through them. Finally he stumbled and fell to his knees, but he continued to crawl through the herd of caribou toward the place where he had last seen Thela.

A giant tree had fallen, and he could dimly see her in the flashes of lightning. She was lying against the tree on the ground. The caribou milled around the tree, but none was close enough to reach the girl with its hoofs.

Dan crawled up and leaned his head against the trunk of the tree, his body partly sheltering her. He drew his breath in great sobs, and stiffened his body against the encroaching caribou, but none actually came close to him.

Hours seemed to have passed before the air became quieter and the pelting rain changed to a steady downpour, and then ceased. Dan had dragged his gun with him, and now it lay beside him, wet and glistening in the faint light. He did not know how long he had remained crouched above the still form of the Indian girl. His legs were so stiff that he no longer felt

L 161

the pain of his cramped position against the log. His whole body had become as immobile as the girl beneath, and he cowered like an animal in a blizzard or a dog waiting over its fallen master.

The forest around him was a place of havoc and wreckage. The bodies of dead caribou lay on the rotting ground where the Indians had killed them. Some were in fairly good condition as far as their skins were concerned; but others were trampled and torn. Everything was marked by the rage of the storm.

Dan looked around but he could see no one. He looked down at the girl on the ground, and there was not a sign of life in the stillness of her face and her glistening skin.

He lifted the lifeless body into his arms and, gripping his gun with one hand, slowly bore her through the trees toward the hunting camp of Komaxala. A few of the Beaver braves stood with the chief, who raised his eyes as Dan emerged from the forest, carrying his burden. Dan went up to the half-broken tent which had been set up for Komaxala, and laid the still form on the grass. The chief stared before him, his eyes barely dropping to the place where the girl lay.

The braves around the Beaver warrior stood silently, but their black eyes gleamed. Out upon the lake the bodies of caribou floated; and in the forest were many more bodies of dead animals. Many of these could be used for hides; and there was much meat. Yet an air of disaster hung over the camp.

They looked at Dan menacingly, as if they only waited for a word from the chief. And in their midst, tall and silent, stood Komaxala. The disaster was great; many of the braves had died in the storm, but of even greater import, most of the herd had escaped. And before the feet of the chief lay the body of his daughter—struck down by lightning that came out of the sky like a thunderbolt of the Great Spirit!

This indeed was disaster. The men who stood around Komaxala felt that this moment could be a turning point in the fate of the Beaver people. Who had to bear the blame? Who had brought disaster? Since the black man had come into the village of the Beavers, he had broken every rule and law of the tribe. He had flouted the sacred laws of the spirits themselves. Was he the bearer of evil?

Had Komaxala done wrong in permitting this black man to remain in the tribe? This was in the mind of each Beaver brave. And now the daughter of the chief had been felled—a woman who had taken forbidden tobacco during a period of penance for the death of her husband. Was this the vengeance of the spirits whose taboos she had violated? The wise men of the Beaver tribe knew that a widow could bring disaster to all around her—as she had, no doubt, brought it to her husband. Why was Thela an exception?

She had eaten of the pot of stew made of the bear's brain. Had this insulted the spirit of the bear? She had smoked from the black man's pipe, and sat by the fire of other hunters, and permitted her face to be lighted and her body warmed by the fire. Was this not enough to drive the spirits of these woods into a mood of revenge? And now she had been killed by lightning! In order to create this revenge, the spirits had wrought havoc among the caribou, destroyed everything in the forest!

These were the things each Beaver brave knew about; and in short words and signs they spoke to each other and to Komaxala. Dan did not understand what they said, but he knew from the angry expressions on their faces and the tone of their voices that there was menace among these people.

He looked down at the girl, and in his heart there was a strange sense of wanting this girl. He had wanted her alive; now that she was dead, he wanted her even more.

Komaxala stood calmly listening to those around him. Bedodid stood beside him, and the two daughterless people remained calm and silent until all had spoken. Komaxala lifted his hand.

The Great Spirit had spoken, he told the other braves. The black scar in the tree, where the fire from the sky had struck at his daughter, was evidence that the Great Spirit had spoken.

But what had the spirit said? Who could know, except one like Ikta, who was still at the village, or the elders of the tribe, such as Kanipaw, who spoke with the wisdom of many winters.

This was a matter for a council. It was evident that terrible forces were at work, and only the combined wisdom of the Beaver people could decide what the meaning of these events might be. The immense tree, split by the lightning, where the daughter of the chief had been struck down, was a sign of the strength of these forces; and so were the dead caribou.

Komaxala made a sign to the others, indicating that the black man was not to be molested. This was the command of the chief, and until a council of braves had decided otherwise, his command would be law in the tribe.

While these things were being said by words and signs, Dan stood looking at the quiet figure of the girl. Under his shirt, against his body, was the tattered Bible. The rain had soaked his clothes, and he knew the Bible must have been damaged; yet there was certainly something in it that could direct his actions now.

He dropped to his knees and prayed for several minutes, but nothing happened. He rolled his eyes toward the sky now and then, as if searching in the gray gloom of the heavens for some kind of token of response, but no heavenly message came. Drops of water continued to fall monotonously upon the leaves of the forest; except for this and a few muttered words which the Beaver braves exchanged between themselves, there was nothing but silence.

Dan finally reached into his shirt, and pulled out the Bible, with its soggy pages. Everything stuck together except the place where the bullet was still imbedded in the pages; and the pages came apart at this point.

Dan stared at the page thus revealed, and read—as he had before:

"Dam . . . rise!"

Dan laid the Bible on the belly of the girl, and bowed his head over her body. His hands were clasped in front of him, so close to his face that his lips almost touched his knuckles.

"Lord . . . Jesus! Make this girl rise like Yo' done for Dan! Make her rise, oh God! It's right here in Yo' Good Book . . . 'He takes the child by the hand' . . . Take Yo' sufferin' child'en by the hand, Jesus, amen!"

Bedodid had come forward, and now she stood beside Dan and laid one hand on his shoulder.

"Black man, our daughter is dead," she said. "*Niuk!* Go away . . . you are of another tribe, and you now have no place in our life."

Dan was praying with feverish intensity, and he paid little attention to Bedodid. He continued to repeat, as if it were some kind of magic word: "Rise, woman . . . fo' the glory of God!" He had run out of new ideas for prayer, and continued to repeat: "Rise, woman, amen! Rise, woman, amen!"

Komaxala stepped forward to intervene, after Dan had failed to follow the command of Bedodid; but at this moment Dan stopped praying, and suddenly leaned down close to the still body of the girl.

Then he raised his head, and stared at the Indians, his eyes full of strange wonder.

"Jesus make her live!" he whispered, his voice low and deep. Suddenly he looked up to the sky again, his eyes rolled and his voice rose to a shout:

"Sweet Jesus . . . Yo' gotta make this miracle! Yo' jes' gotta. . . ."

Around the strange tableau the trees wept silently on the soft, wet ground. The skies were closer, from the rising mists of early morning; and the tall, glistening trees rose like monuments among the scattered and dismembered bodies of the dead caribou. In the midst of this assembly of natural grief and death stood the chief and his wife and the Beaver braves. At their feet knelt the black giant over the still body of the Indian girl. The muscles of his huge jaw worked like thongs under the skin, as he turned his eyes toward the sky and prayed, mumbling and roaring in alternate moods of despair and hope.

The heavens seemed to stir at Dan's violent prayer. The

165

words came from between his clenched teeth as if they were wrenched from his soul; and his black eyes, rimmed with white, searched the sky for some sign that "sweet Jesus" had heard his prayer.

One of the Indians stepped closer and pointed to the girl. Then he muttered something sharply, and looked at the chief. Komaxala himself came forward and bent over Dan's crouched figure, and stared at the girl.

Then with sudden firmness he put his hand on Dan's shoulder, as if to pull him away from the girl. But Dan leaned closer to Thela; and his immense bulk was immovable. He put his finger in his mouth and held it over the girl's mouth. Then he suddenly stood up.

"Yo' daughter ain't dead!" he roared to Komaxala so loudly that the chief seemed to be more startled by the sound of Dan's voice than the sense of what he said. "She ain't dead!" Dan roared. "She ain't dead!"

The mother, Bedodid, always calm and disciplined, thrust her way past Komaxala and Dan. She flung herself across the body of the girl, her ear close to Thela's breast. The tears so long held back came now like a gushet after rain has washed over parched ground. She lay on the body of her daughter, sobbing a strange chant . . . the song an Indian woman sings to produce new life when she is in labor with a child.

CHAPTER FOURTEEN

It was some time before Dan was aware of the things that were happening around him. He saw Bedodid, lying on the wet ground holding the head of her daughter; then she stood up, pressing her clenched hands against her face, so that her face was smeared with mud. Spruce needles from the wet ground were glued to her face and hair, and she began to scream in a way that startled the other Indians.

Several of the braves moved closer to the girl, pressing around Dan and pushing him away from the mother and daughter. One of them cried out that it was forbidden to take back the dead from the Great Spirit, and aimed a shaking finger at Dan. Two young braves, their minds tortured beyond control, ran into the forest, shouting wildly that the spirits were chasing them, and there was nothing to do but run.

These two men ran until they reached the village of the Beavers, and began beating on the tent of Ikta. He came out and attempted to calm them. Then he heard the story of the strange happenings at the hunting camp.

Ikta listened, unable to understand everything; but he knew it was now time for him to join the hunters at the camp near the lake where the caribou had been found. The old medicine man was gravely concerned. Ever since Attalu had raised his hand against the chief of the Beavers, and had been exiled, things had not gone well. The spirits were evidently angry; and now this black man had come into the village and broken all the laws and taboos, and the old gods of his people were unquestionably angry and disgusted.

Ikta decided that the first step to be taken was to rid the tribe of this black guest, who had infected everyone with madness and now even presumed to raise the dead—a performance that Ikta secretly envied, since he had never been able to duplicate it. Some way must be found to get the black sorcerer out of the village. And Ikta knew that in order to do this, he must oppose Komaxala.

Ikta spoke with old Kanipaw, the wisest of the elders of the tribe, before he left.

"It would be well for you to follow me in a few days to the hunting camp," he said. "As soon as the boiling of *klina* is finished, you should come so that there can be a Council of Braves over these strange matters."

Kanipaw was a man of practical wisdom. He was not a medicine man or sorcerer, as Ikta was; but his words were always heeded in the councils. If he should advise Komaxala to give up his position as chief, for the good of the Beaver tribe, there could be no question about it: Komaxala would step down. If this should happen, Ikta might very easily become the chief. Both were very conscious of this possibility, but neither mentioned it.

When Ikta reached the lake, the excitement had abated to some extent. The braves were occupied with skinning the caribou; and some had paddled in canoes across the lake to the island, where there were still some remnants of the herd. The question of Komaxala's position with the tribe did not seem to have been raised; he was still the chief.

Ikta went directly to Komaxala, who lay in his tent, considerably weakened by the series of events.

"The rumor has reached our village that strange things have happened," Ikta said. Komaxala nodded gravely.

"What has happened to your daughter will require a meeting of the Council of Braves," Ikta went on. His wrinkled face betrayed no emotion except for his eyes, which burned feverishly. Everyone knew that when the medicine man of the tribe asked for a Council of Braves, great events were in the making.

Komaxala lifted a hand to indicate he understood Ikta's request.

Then Ikta went over to Dan, who sat cleaning his rifle. He touched the shoulder of the Negro, but Dan did not lift his head or change his position. Ikta took a stronger hold on Dan's shoulder, and attempted to wrench him around. Dan, with a sweeping movement of his arm, struck the old Indian's hand from his shoulder. The medicine man staggered back from the blow.

"Lemme alone!" Dan said, glaring at the Indian. "Don' ever touch Dan that way!"

Ikta said, "I wish to speak with you, black man!"

Dan shrugged, and turned his head. For a moment he resumed his work, disregarding Ikta's presence. Ikta's seamed face twisted and the smoldering rage within him suddenly seemed to burst from his eyes. His face was distorted with a snarling expression, a rare thing among Indians.

168

"Black man, you stand on the edge of the world of spirits!"
Ikta shouted, in Beaver. He turned and saw a hatchet lying in
front of Dan's tent, and he stooped and seized it.

Dan looked up and saw the Indian, with hatchet raised,
ready to strike. The big Negro climbed quickly to his feet.

"You have come among our people and violated our rules,"
Ikta continued in tense tones. "You have sought to turn our
people against each other, and you have defied the laws of
the spirits of our tribe. You must die so that the spirits will
look upon us with favor once more!"

The braves stood around, watching this strange scene. Only
one person moved. This was Bedodid, who came forward and
stood between the black visitor and the infuriated medicine
man.

"Do not touch this man," she said quietly. "His power has
called my daughter back to life. If his power is greater than
yours, it is you who must step back . . . This man's medicine
is not finished. My daughter does not speak!"

She spoke calmly, yet her face seemed to glow with sudden
fire, and there was vibrant authority in her voice that no one
in the village could ignore.

Ikta, however, was past all reasoning.

"Let the black man show us if his power is good for himself!" he shouted, raising the hatchet and trying to get past
Bedodid without striking at her. Dan had stepped back toward
a fallen tree trunk, where he had laid his gun.

"Ne'mine now, Jesus," he muttered. "Dan is a-goin' to take
care of this hisself!"

He knew his gun was loaded, and he lifted it from the trunk.
He swung it around so the muzzle pointed at old Ikta. The
medicine man, who had given way to the black visitor only
because he feared Komaxala's anger, lost all restraint.

"You will die, black man!" he roared, and at the same instant
he gave a great bound to one side, so that Bedodid was no
longer standing between himself and Dan. Almost in a continuous motion, the lithe old body seemed to coil and spring

169

forward again, this time directly toward Dan. The hatchet was upraised, but he never brought it down.

Dan fired and the Indian's body seemed to double in mid-air from the impact of the bullet against his stomach. He crumpled to the ground, and lay in an awkward heap, the hatchet still clutched in his hand.

The other Beaver braves moved forward, silently and without haste. This event was so unprecedented that none wished to take any action, beyond staring at the dead man. The killing of a medicine man was unheard of among the Beavers; it indicated that strange events were happening, and in such cases Indians would not act without taking counsel with one another.

Only Komaxala moved. He had been standing near his tent when Bedodid stepped out, and he made no move to restrain her. Wounded as he was, Komaxala still was the ruling authority among the Beavers, and no action would be taken by any brave without his direction.

He now came forward to the place where Ikta lay.

It seemed that this day was filled with remarkable events. As Komaxala came forward, there was a scream from across the encampment.

Two women had come from Thela's grass-thatched hut, where she had lain, as immobile as death itself, barely breathing. These women had started across the clearing toward Ikta. They were two of the "unclean" women who had followed the others to the camp; and now one of them had turned and screamed.

Thela stood in the opening of the hut. Whether it was the sound of the shot, or strange forces that filled the air, no Beaver could determine; but they saw at once that Thela now was fully alive, standing in the door of the hut.

She lifted one arm and then let it fall to her side. It was at this point that it became noticeable that Thela's face was not normal. One side was drawn up, so that it distorted her mouth and gave the effect of half smile and half frown. The muscles of her neck on the side that was drawn up were tight as

170

thongs drawn under her skin, and her eye on the same side was stretched, as if a string had been attached to the lower part of the eye and drawn downward through her cheek.

Bedodid turned as the woman screamed, and then ran to her daughter's side. Komaxala stood beside the body of Ikta, looking at his wife and daughter.

Dan had quickly shoved another bullet into the loading chamber of his gun. He stood with the gun poised, and a certain grimness had replaced the usual grin on his face. He had seen only part of what had transpired, but now he saw that Thela had come out of her hut and was standing unaided.

The Beaver braves turned toward the woman, and were staring at her in astonishment. It was evident that she had not merely returned from the dead; she appeared to have returned fully alive, with the strength of the living . . . except for the side of her face, which was drawn into a strange semblance of a smile.

Dan realized that the resurrection of Thela had now drawn all attention from himself. He let his gun fall into a resting position under his arm. He was trying to rack his brain for some way of turning these remarkable events to his advantage.

His curiosity was also stirred by the sight of Thela's face. The Indian women of the camp were now standing around her; Bedodid spoke to her, and with her fingers caressed the girl's face. Thela did not move, nor by any sign or expression of her eyes indicate that she saw any of them.

Her almost unseeing eyes were fixed on Dan, and now she stepped forward out of the ring of women around her. Her mother tried to keep her back, but Thela glided gracefully to one side and came forward toward Dan.

Her mouth seemed to twitch convulsively, as though she were attempting an unfamiliar word or sound, but no sound issued from her lips. Dan suddenly realized, with a kind of horror, that she could not speak.

Thela walked like one who is sleeping. Her face was entirely calm on one side but distorted on the other; and she moved as if she had no strength in her own body but was

171

propelled by some unseen force. When she was a few feet from Dan she stopped, and still no sound issued from her.

At this instant another unexpected thing happened. There was the noise of whistling in the trees, and several figures emerged from the forest. The Beaver braves stood irresolutely; so much had happened that there were no normal signals to guide them. Even Komaxala had become irresolute.

The newcomers were led by Kanipaw, the wisest of the elders, who had followed Ikta from the Beaver village. His old eyes swept the scene, finally coming to rest upon the face of Komaxala, who once again stood erect, with the commanding authority of a chief.

Each raised a hand, and grunted. Without speaking, Kanipaw turned toward Komaxala's tent and the chief followed him. The two disappeared into the tent, and none of the other Beaver braves followed.

Dan knew least of all those present what was going on. He had turned to watch the new arrivals as they entered the clearing; but now he was looking again at Thela.

The girl was still beautiful, in spite of the strange distortion of her face. Her hair, black as a raven's wing, lay close to her head and was held in two knots which her mother had plaited for her when she was lying helpless in the thatched tent. Her body was still straight and tall, and she stood as still as a young spruce tree in the quiet of the forest. Yet her eyes had changed; they no longer were alight with inner fires but seemed to look unseeingly upon the world.

At the arrival of Kanipaw she had stopped walking forward and now she stood a few feet from where the body of Ikta lay; but she looked beyond him at the rim of the forest. Dan moved closer to her, and finally he said in a mumbling voice:

"Yo' is my woman now, ain't yo'?"

The girl did not answer, but her eyes moved for an instant toward Dan. He could think of nothing further to say, having more or less declared himself; he fumbled with the Bible inside his shirt and stared at the girl, who stared unseeingly beyond him.

172

Kanipaw emerged from Komaxala's tent. He looked briefly at the body of the dead medicine man, who was in a way his rival for position as the wisest man of the tribe; but it was not for an Indian to express either sorrow or exultation. The honor of Ikta was now a matter for the judgment of the spirits, not for any mortal man.

A fire was gathered and Ikta's body placed upon it. After the fire had burned down, and the young braves who would watch over the cremated ashes throughout the night in honor of the dead medicine man had taken their positions around the embers, Kanipaw raised his hand as a signal that he had something to say.

"When the rain has washed the ashes of this man into the ground, his spirit will return to the land of his forefathers," the old brave said, in a slow voice that was almost like a chant. "May his life in the hunting ground of old warriors be happy and filled with those things that delight the heart of a brave!"

Kanipaw then went into the hut Ikta had built for himself. He was an older man than Ikta; and although he did not possess the active spirit of the dead man, which led him to explore the secrets of the spirits and advise the Beavers of the ways and attitudes of the spirits, nevertheless Kanipaw was a man of deep wisdom and great experience, and his words were greatly respected.

Thela had gone back to the tent where her mother sat beside her; but the girl still had not uttered a word. Her eyes moved from place to place, and she made signs with her hands, which indicated she heard what was being said. But she had lost the power to talk.

Kanipaw came into the tent, and Bedodid arose silently and left. The old man stood for some time, speaking to the girl in a low voice which did not carry beyond the door of the hut. Later he left the hut, and went back to the tent of Ikta, which he had taken as his own. He signaled that the door should be closed and laced tightly, so that neither man nor spirit might enter to disturb his thoughts.

For many hours Kanipaw remained in the hut, and at times

173

the sound of his voice could be heard, rising in a strange chant, composed of words that were not familiar to the Beavers. No one was allowed to look into the tent, nor was a stone to be lifted or a fire started or even a skin scraped during these hours of meditation. It was known by everyone that Kanipaw would speak with the spirits; and when he had discovered the will of the spirits, he would seek to bind the decisions of the tribe to their will.

During the night the watchmen kept vigil around the hut, but no one sought to listen. The very twigs of the trees in the forest seemed to have become stiffened in the tension of silence, and the young braves on watch sat in equally silent terror, fearful that the spirits were active in the night.

Shortly after dawn the next morning Kanipaw pushed aside the willow branches laced across the door of the hut. His face was drawn and he seemed to have aged during the night. His voice was weak, and he asked for some water to drink. This was brought in a skin which was spread out before him so that he could scoop the water with his hands.

After drinking, he walked directly to the tent of Komaxala, and here the braves formed around him in a circle, with the women standing in a larger circle behind the men. This was a Council of Braves, to which the women of the tribe might listen. Kanipaw even ordered that the four "unclean" women be present, and Thela stood closest to him except for Bedodid, who stood behind her husband.

This was a solemn affair. Much that had happened would now be explained; and the decisions of the council taken this day would be binding on all people of the Beaver tribe forever. Outside the group, standing alone with his rifle, was the black visitor, whose arrival at the village had introduced a chain of portentous events such as no Beaver alive could remember. Many questions had to be decided, but the most important concerned the black visitor. Did he come with the powers of the spirits of the forest, or did he come as an alien, bringing evil to the home of the Beavers? Everything hinged upon this one point. . . .

174

Kanipaw spoke.

"Some strange things have happened," he said slowly, "requiring the greatest wisdom of the warriors and the elders of the Beaver tribe to counsel us so that we may follow the wishes of the spirits of the forest. The Great Spirit has sent us a herd of caribou—such a gift as few Beavers have known, and one that would stay the dangers of hunger for many moons!

"The Great Spirit has given us this gift, and since there must be a balance in nature, the Great Spirit must take from us one of our people . . . First, the spirit of the sky spoke in a loud voice and struck down one of us, the daughter of a chief. This fire is caused by a mighty stone wedged against a flint high up in the ridges of the Great Mountains. The stone and the flint strike fire . . . and such a fire can be aimed a long distance and strike death at a man or a woman.

"Yet, observe what happened! The fire was sent from the mountains and it struck the girl, who is the daughter of the chief. She wore the clothes of a warrior at the time, having thrown off her own clothing in the lake during the storm. The spirit of the fire struck at her when she wore the clothes of a brave. But spirits cannot be deceived by men. Other things had happened, such as the eating of the brains of the bear by a woman, which has never happened before; and the smoking of tobacco given to her at a time when she could not take such a gift from anyone but her mother.

"These were strange events, and the spirit of the fire that struck at this girl wished us to know that the spirits cannot be deceived. Yet she is now alive, and we must ask, Why is that? Why does she whom the spirit struck down still live among us?

"There are many secrets the spirits hold among themselves, and we cannot be told these secrets until we join our forefathers in their hunting grounds. But observe this: the girl was sent back to life again!

"The spirits do not wish a girl where a man is expected. But in order to prevent her from telling how it is to be dead, the spirits have sealed her lips . . . and so it will be for many years, until she has forgotten what she has seen.

"And now a man whom the spirits called has gone, and the ashes of his body are sinking into the ground. This is the punishment of the Beaver tribe for permitting a girl to wear the clothes of a man. That is why Ikta is dead . . . He should have taught the Beavers not to put the clothes of a man upon a woman. His death was therefore a punishment to all of us, and no man may be blamed for it. . . ."

The old Indian paused, his black eyes darting in a continuous sweep around the circle of faces, as if he would impart his message to every living Beaver within his view. Then, in the same low, monotonous voice, he went on.

"There are two kinds of laws that the spirits give to us. One is the law of the Beavers, that we must know and follow. But there is another kind of law for those who know nothing of our customs . . . who are often foolish and do what is wrong in our eyes. It is wise for Beavers to obey the laws of the Beavers, but it is also wise not to expect such actions of those who do not understand our laws. Soon the spirits themselves will decide what to do in such cases."

He looked at Komaxala; and although the chief did not betray by so much as a flicker of his eyes what was in his mind, a message passed between the two. Dan, leaning on his rifle, understood nothing. He continued to listen, however, and to stare at Thela.

"Now as to what lies ahead," Kanipaw continued. "Do not permit such things to happen again. If a woman is allowed to wear a man's clothes, will the Beavers then send women into battle? Are girls to hunt the bears in the forest?"

He paused again, and there was a gleam in his old eyes as he looked at the faces of the braves, ringed around him.

"Do not give an insult to nature! Do not insult the spirits of the forest, nor the spirit of the bear! Let women fish and sew and give birth to our children . . . but never let a woman try to be like a man! The spirits will not permit us to try to deceive them again!

"I have spoken."

CHAPTER FIFTEEN

Dan had stood silently while Kanipaw delivered words of wise counsel, understanding neither the words nor the sense of them. His heavy features dropped into a kind of sullen repose; his eyes moved from face to face, fixing longest upon the face of Thela, who stared unseeingly above the heads of the others.

He had no intention of letting his miracle pass unnoticed by the Beavers; yet again he felt a strange barrier, a hostility that was like a smoldering fire between him and the warriors of the Beaver tribe. No one spoke to him, or even by a glance disclosed the gratitude that must have been felt by the Beavers.

Had he not brought the daughter of the chief back to life? Had he not saved the life of the chief from the attack of the grizzly bear? Had he not brought meat to their camp—animals killed with his rifle, that shot so straight no animal could escape his bullets?

These were things that any man might brag about—and upon which the firm friendship of the people of the Beaver tribe should rest. And yet Dan was aware that the Beaver braves not only did not accept his acts with the respect and adulation they deserved, but there was a hostility toward him which he could not understand—and which he did not like.

Shortly after Kanipaw finished his speech to the Beaver tribe, several hunters paddled across the lake to the islands where the caribou still grazed. Dan followed them, thankful of this return to action. He knew that his rifle would speak even louder than his prayers, or the words of Kanipaw; accordingly he made certain that the Indians watched each shot. The Indians had to load their guns with ramrods, but Dan could shoot as rapidly as he was able to shove one cartridge

M

after another into the breech of his Sharps rifle. Furthermore, the Indians had to get close to the caribou to hit them, whereas Dan could stand off at a distance and knock over an animal every time he fired.

His shots confused the caribou, who could not see the source of death that struck among them; and Dan proudly continued, shot after shot, demonstrating his mastery with a gun. He brought in more meat than the women could handle, and it was necessary for the younger braves to cut up the game and carry it home. The following day the melting pots bubbled brightly with tallow, and skins were laid out on the stones to dry.

Seldom had the outlook been so bright for the Beavers; and it was accepted by all that Kanipaw had spoken the truth, and that the spirits of the forest were now satisfied to have taken the life of Ikta as a punishment of all the Beavers.

The caribou tried several times to break away from the island, but those which attempted to swim to shore were shot, and the others turned in fear and raced back toward the middle of the island, where they awaited methodical slaughter by the Beavers. Dan shot so often that he did not realize that for each caribou he must spend a bullet.

Finally Dan shot his last bullet; after that he was subdued, since he had nothing to remind the Indians constantly of his superior powers. Thela had fully regained consciousness, and except for her twisted face—and the fact that she could not talk—it might have been supposed that she had never undergone the ordeal of death.

When most of the caribou on the island had been killed, the Beaver hunters began to prepare the dried meat and pots of tallow for the journey back to the village. When the meat had been dried and cut into small pieces, tallow was pressed into the meat, making a delicious pemmican. The meat and tallow pieces were stored in the stomachs of the caribou, which gave the young braves the impression that a war might be in the making, since these were provisions for traveling.

No word was spoken about war from the mouths of the

chief and the elder warriors of the tribe, however; and if a war was being prepared, it was a dark secret among the leaders.

Dan meanwhile found himself without ammunition, and consequently without a subject upon which to talk. He had established himself as a great hunter, but without bullets to demonstrate his prowess, his feeling of self-satisfaction soon wore off. He trudged across the valleys with the other hunters toward the Beaver village, silent and sullen. It seemed to him that no matter how remarkable his acts were, he always suffered the galling bitterness of defeat.

Dan had learned to speak and understand the Beaver language sufficiently to converse about ordinary subjects, although he was unable to follow the more difficult phrases of Kanipaw; and he found his companionship with the Beaver braves quite pleasant, as long as he did not talk about himself. But he could not help speaking of his own prowess, waving his hand toward the forest and crying out, "We gonna have plenty of meat this winter—and Dan is gonna get it, yes sir!" At these times, the Beaver braves fell silent, or found other matters to discuss among themselves.

There was, of course, the small matter of bullets. Dan had none, and he was not quite sure how he could get them, but at present he had no use for the gun anyway. When he reached the Beaver camp he decided to devote himself to fishing.

This can be a tiresome sport for a man given to talking a great deal. Dan found it difficult to explain his prowess as a fisherman, since the fish came to him, not he to them. Besides, small boys standing near him often caught more fish than he did.

One day Dan saw Thela walking along the beach, below the village, and he motioned for her to follow him into the forest. The girl looked at him for a moment, and then she reached down and took the hand of a small girl at her side. Together they followed Dan into the forest.

Dan found a willow tree and scraped some bark for "knickkneck." He handed the scrapings to Thela, and she took them submissively, then followed him back to the village. Dan was strangely perplexed at her attitude; it seemed to him that as her savior—the one who had called upon the power of God to bring her back to life—he should have been followed with more willingness, and perhaps without the small girl as an escort.

Dan lived in his hut with the blind boy, Gnanisk, as his constant companion. The young brave followed Dan around the village like a dog. He was able to make his way alone across the village, using a willow stick to guide his feet; but whenever Dan emerged from the tent, Gnanisk forgot everything else and followed the giant black man.

Gnanisk stayed out of the way of everyone who came to the hut. He moved as silently as a shadow, carving arrows and twining fishlines for Dan. He could cut skins into the finest thongs, using his fingers that were as sensitive as the feelers of an insect. He sharpened knives until they were so keen they could cut a hair; and in every small task he excelled everyone else in the village.

But these were small tasks. Gnanisk would never be able to match his skill with other hunters because he would never hunt. He was useful, however, to keep the tent clean and to prepare food.

One day Dan spoke to Komaxala about the lack of ammunition.

"Maybe yo' got some skins yo' could trade for a few bullets," he said. "I shot a hell of a lot of them caribous, an' there ought to be a few skins left."

Komaxala regarded the black man thoughtfully. Since Kanipaw had made his declaration before the Council of Braves, there had been less hostility against the black stranger; but Komaxala was wise enough to understand that this was not a permanent thing. Dan had been given little chance to brag, owing to his lack of ammunition for his gun; but given an opportunity, there was no doubt the Negro would resume his familiar speeches.

"Beaver tribe has many braves," Komaxala finally said, in

180

a slow, patient voice. "But Beavers do not have many skins. If many Beavers go to white man's fort with few skins, white man will be angry. If one black man go with many skins, white man will be happy."

Komaxala knew the foolishness of the white man in judging the worth of skins. If a single Indian brought one skin, the white traders would feel cheated—even though the skin might be of the finest quality. If many Indians came, each with one skin, the feeling of being cheated would be multiplied by the number of Indians.

But if one man brought many skins, the white traders would feel gratified even if the hair was ready to fall off the skins. It was desirable not to change this stupidity; consequently the Beavers often piled their skins before the chief, and he and one or two warriors would offer them for trade, thus being assured of striking a bargain which, in its final result, would be to the advantage of the Beavers.

In this case it might be possible that the black stranger would be able to trade a small number of skins of poor quality for bullets. There was also another advantage to be considered; the expedition to Fort St. John might lead to the permanent departure of Dan from the village. Komaxala considered these points carefully as he spoke.

"This is now time for building winter houses," the chief said, watching Dan through the slits of his half-closed eyes. "Beaver braves must prepare fish and pemmican. Maybe a great hunter will go to white man's village and trade a few skins for bullets . . . The Beavers have a few skins which might be found for such a journey."

Komaxala said nothing more, waiting for his words to take effect.

Dan understood the chief's words; but he had his own problems to consider. He did not know whether it would be wise for him to return alone to Fort St. John. He had now become a great hunter, and was about to take a chief's daughter as his mate! He was no longer a slave. Such a man could not endure being treated as an inferior.

Dan had a feeling that the efficacy of prayer would be of little use against the prejudice of white men. Possibly this was due to the fact that the white men were on the same side of God that Dan was. At any rate, it had been his experience that no amount of praying or begging stayed the hand of a white man with a whip.

It was a matter to be thought about; so Dan rose to his feet and told Komaxala he would wait a while before giving his answer. That night he spoke to Gnanisk.

"Yo' like to go some place in a canoe?" he asked. Gnanisk turned his sightless eyes toward Dan and nodded mutely. He would go anywhere with his master and protector.

"Yo' is gonna be my boy—jes' takin' care of my house," Dan went on. "The white man's law says ev'ybody is free, but yo' ain't like ev'ybody—yo' is like an Indian that ain't got no home, an' yo' belongs to me."

Again Gnanisk nodded. He was bound to Dan not only by gratitude and tribal law but by necessity. Except for his wooden stick with which he was able to direct his steps, he had no one to guide him.

"Gnanisk good man in canoe," he finally said, in a low voice. "Where my father goes, I go!"

Dan nodded, his heavy lips splitting in a grin of satisfaction. It was always a matter of satisfaction to him when anyone paid him a tribute, no matter how small or how unimportant the one who paid the tribute.

"Dan always gonna get meat," he said. "On'y thing now, Dan ain't got any bullets, an' we gotta eat fish."

The following day a curious thing happened outside the tent of Komaxala. Osawask, one of the three young braves Dan had encountered on the beach at Fort St. John, approached the chief and spoke to him in a loud voice, so that all could hear.

"I am ready to find out if the luck of Komaxala is greater than mine," Osawask said, pretentiously. He produced a piece of tobacco. "Let me risk my last piece of tobacco."

Dan, who had come up to Komaxala's tent during this exchange, stood near the pair. He saw Komaxala nod gravely, and the chief then produced a piece of tobacco. They drew sticks, and Komaxala won.

"It is a strange thing," Osawask said, still speaking loudly, "but the best dog in the village belongs not to the chief but to me. Perhaps the great chief will try his luck again, and he may be able to own my dog."

Komaxala nodded again, and they drew sticks once more. Once again, the chief won. Dan, staring at this exchange of property, felt sorry for Osawask. Not a word was spoken for some time. The other braves who stood around looked at each other knowingly. Everyone in the village—except Dan—knew that this was an application on the part of Osawask to become a member of the chief's family.

That night Osawask presented himself at the chief's hut, carrying a blanket. He spread this inside the door of the chief's tent and squatted upon it. With a gesture of his hand, Osawask made it plain by words and signs that he had come to partake of Komaxala's hospitality.

"The lice are biting in my tent," he explained. "It is better to rest here."

Komaxala nodded, and then said in a patient voice:

"It will be interesting to see how differently the lice in this house behave. You may explain the difference to me when you have tried them."

This was the permission Osawask sought; he lay down and soon was fast asleep. Thela, sitting on the other side of the tent, understood Osawask's intentions; but she also understood that it was the custom of the Beaver people to allow a woman to choose for herself whom she would have as a husband. Her father had indicated that Osawask was the man of his choice; yet his words did not in any way commit Thela to this decision.

After a few moments had passed, during which Osawask's snores—whether natural or otherwise—rose to a crescendo of sound, so that they could be heard from the surrounding tents, Thela also lay down to sleep. But she chose a location for her blanket on the side of the tent farthest from Osawask. This was a definite indication that Thela had refused to be Osawask's mate.

When those in the tent awakened in the morning, Osawask and his blanket had disappeared. He, too, understood Thela's answer.

It was not long before these events were known to Dan. Gnanisk, whose ears were as long as his sight was short, heard the words of other Indians, and reported to his black master that the daughter of the chief had been sought by Osawask, but his suit had been rejected.

This might have pleased Dan, but instead it sent him into a rage. He strode out of his tent and across the village to the large tent of Komaxala. The chief showed no surprise at the suddenness of Dan's visit. He remained seated, calmly shaving a small piece of wood he had been carving into a tool for his house. With a slight gesture of his hand, he indicated that Dan should say what was in his mind.

Dan lost no time coming to the point.

"Yo' daughter would be daid today, ef'n it weren't for me!" he blurted out. "I raised her from the daid, with the help of Jesus!"

Komaxala lifted a placating hand.

"My daughter does not speak," he said. "She cannot tell all that she has experienced; therefore we cannot know how she was returned from the hunting grounds beyond the forest."

Dan, standing in front of the chief, was aware that Komaxala had gained a tactical advantage by remaining seated. The women in the tent—Bedodid and Thela—sat motionless, scraping skins and giving little attention to anything but their domestic tasks. Yet Dan knew from the careful way they sat, hunched before a small fire that burned in the center of the hut, that they were well aware of his mission.

"Me—Dan'l Williams!" he said, in a rumbling voice, pounding his chest with his huge hand. "I understand her, 'cause I brung her back to the land o' the livin'—yo' understand that?"

Komaxala nodded politely.

"She belong to me, by the rights of Almighty God," Dan continued.

There was a longer period of silence. Thela, by training and instinct, did not reveal by so much as a flicker of her eyes that she knew she was the subject of this extraordinary proposal. But her fingers moved swiftly, and her thoughts moved even more swiftly.

"Your behavior is unusual," Komaxala was saying to Dan. "But that in itself is no longer unusual to us. Your ability as a hunter is well known. Your long gun speaks with swiftness and brings death to the farthest animals. But you often act in other ways like a child. You speak of another God Who is stronger than the spirits of the Beaver tribe. This I do not know . . . There are many men among your people who say this. In some ways your people are strong, and in other ways they are weak."

He hesitated, as if to let this simple peroration sink in. Dan was paying little attention, mumbling snatches of phrases to himself with sudden anger, but not daring openly to interrupt the chief.

"She belong to me!" he finally muttered, with some stubbornness.

"The Council of Braves must decide upon a question that concerns the power of your God and that of the Great Spirit of our people," Komaxala said; apparently he was about to expatiate upon this point when Thela herself rose from the ground.

She reached up to a shelf above her and took several items, including pieces of tobacco and other things, which she placed carefully in a bag. No one else in the tent spoke or moved as she performed this sudden act. Then she walked across the tent and handed the bag to Dan.

He took them, staring at her with his eyes wide open. He was about to speak, but she quickly bent down and picked up two blankets from the ground. Then she took a leather jacket from the place where it hung against the wall, and with her free hand pushed Dan toward the door.

Komaxala, in spite of his weakness, leaped to his feet with

185

surprising alacrity. He made another leap toward the door; but Dan with a single sweep of his hand sent the chief sprawling to one side, and before Komaxala could regain his feet, Dan and the girl had passed out of the hut.

Komaxala had snatched his knife from his belt, and he remained at his door with the weapon poised in his hand. There were many in the Beaver camp who might have speculated on what was passing through the mind of the great chief. His face was like graven stone as he watched the hulking figure of the Negro moving in long clumsy strides beside the lithe form of the Indian girl.

There had been many instances in the experience of this great Beaver warrior in which he had seen violence done upon a white man. There was a day at Fort Vermilion when an Indian threw a knife at the back of a white trader; the blade sank up to the haft in the man's back . . . yet the trader recovered, and that winter terrible starvation was visited upon the Indians of his tribe. No one could foresee the power of the white man's medicine . . .

Dan had entered his hut, with the girl behind him, when Komaxala turned and went back into his own tent, the knife still clutched in his hand. Dan stood for several minutes inside his tent. On a blanket lay the Indian boy, Gnanisk, his blank eyes turned in the direction of his master, seeking to sense by that intimate understanding that belongs to those who have been deprived of a normal sense, exactly what had happened. He knew Thela was in the tent because he could smell her presence.

Dan, for his part, was absorbed in thought. His untutored mind was strangely balanced in things that had to do with nature. He was now in a small world—his own house—with two other people, one sightless and the other mute. He was the only whole person in the tent, and Dan knew this placed a new responsibility upon him. He must thereafter supply these missing senses . . . and by virtue of this alone, these people were bound to him for life. The inhabitants of this tent were neither three people nor one; but they were three in one

186

. . . It was like the Holy Trinity of God, and he—Dan—was in a certain sense the representative of God in this house.

This notion did no violence whatever to Dan's natural piety. It was as easy to think of himself as a representative of God—a minor God, in a way—as it was for him to address Jesus personally in prayer.

"Yo' both belongs to Dan," he said, in a low, deep voice; and Gnanisk knew from the depths of his sightless understanding, just as Thela saw from the serious composure of his thickly molded face, that Dan had become a father to them.

"Now we gonna get some bullets," Dan continued. "I gonna get me a army o' people, an' we goin' to Fort St. John for bullets."

The idea was only half-formed at first, but it soon became a plan. Dan thought of this plan for several days before he again addressed Komaxala.

"Yo' spoke about some beaver skins fo' tradin'," he said to the chief. Komaxala nodded.

"I is gonna take my wife——" Dan hesitated, not knowing whether this was the proper term to use; but as the chief's face betrayed no thoughts on the matter, he went on: "I is gonna take my wife an' the boy—an' maybe somebody else—an' we goin' upriver to the fort."

Komaxala nodded again, although his expression still showed neither assent nor dissent. Finally he spoke:

"It is well that the son of the black spirit is going to get some more bullets," he said. "With his gun, he is a great hunter. Without it, he is a child in the woods. His greatness lies in the shooting of his gun, and without bullets, even the gun is not great. But as a warrior, he should go alone—and leave the squaw and the boy at home."

He spoke in Beaver, but Dan understood the gist of what he said. His face settled into a surly frown; he did not like the intimation that his greatness was only in his gun; nor did he like to be instructed as to who should go with him.

"The Lord ain't gonna let Dan suffer without no bullets," he said. "Yo' remembers it was the Lord that raised yo' daughter f'om the daid . . . Yo' ain't got enough medicine in the whole damn Beaver nation to beat the Lord!"

Komaxala's face still was expressionless.

"Perhaps the power of the God of your people can be shown in other ways . . . Tomorrow there will be a festival in honor of my daughter who is now your woman. Food will be prepared so that all who enter the contests will be strong. Do you see that stone, son of the black spirit?"

He pointed to a round, smooth stone which lay a few feet out in the lake, partly submerged. Dan looked at the stone, his face contracting in a puzzled frown. He knew the chief had something in mind, and he was trying to figure out in advance what it might be so that he would be prepared to answer properly—and to his own advantage.

Komaxala explained: The great stone was the final test of strength for Beaver braves. No Indian had been able to lift it. Perhaps the son of the black spirit, as a final test of the power of his God, would be able to do this.

Dan walked down to the edge of the lake and looked at the stone. It was smooth and heavy, and weighed several hundred pounds. It was lodged against the bottom near the shore in a way that indicated it had been there for some time.

Late that day Thela left Dan's hut and disappeared into the forest. He did not notice her absence until some time later; then he questioned Gnanisk, but received no satisfactory reply. Late in the evening she returned, carrying in a small leather sack some yellow substance. She poured this on the ground and mixed it with water, making a thick, yellow glue.

The following morning the festival began. After some games, which included throwing heavy spears and foot-racing, Komaxala indicated that any brave who wished to do so might match his strength against the stone in the lake.

Two young Indians ran into the water, and each tried in turn to move the stone. They succeeded in moving it slightly, but neither could lift it from the water. While they stood in the water, shaking their heads at their defeat, there was a sound from the Indians on the shore. From a place farther along the beach a tall Indian, followed by a dog, strode into the water.

It was Osawask. He looked disdainfully at the two young braves, who stood aside in crestfallen silence. He turned to the shore and remarked in a loud voice that those nearest the water should stand back, since he might hurl the stone ashore and injure some of them.

The Indians laughed and moved back. Thela, who had come down to the beach with Dan, stood behind him. Tied to her belt was the leather bag.

Osawask turned and looked directly at the girl.

"Perhaps the proud daughter of the chief will agree to sleep on the blanket of a man who can lift the stone!" he shouted; then he stooped and put his powerful arms around the stone.

Osawask tugged and strained, until the muscles stood out like ropes along his shoulders and back. His face glistened as if he had plunged it into the water at his feet, but the stone barely moved. Once he seemed to have gotten it off the bottom, but the smooth sides slipped under the grasp of his fingers.

Finally he turned, his face barely showing the agony of his body at this tremendous effort. The Indians on shore shouted and laughed, and finally Osawask walked back in the direction from which he had come.

Komaxala stood on the shore, and now he looked directly at Dan.

"Is the medicine of the son of the black spirit strong enough to lift this stone?" he asked. "Or is it as weak as that of Osawask?"

Dan had watched these proceedings carefully. While all the attention was being centered on Osawask, he had felt something on his hands, and then he observed that Thela had reached into the leather bag at her waist and taken out some of the yellow substance, which she had rubbed on his hands. His palms felt heavy and when he closed his fists, he found that his fingers stuck together.

Holding his fists closed, Dan waded into the water. He was much taller than Osawask. His big head hunched forward on his shoulders, and his long arms swung loosely as he shambled across the water toward the stone. On the beach Kanipaw spoke a brief ritual, calling upon the spirits to witness whether the strength of any man was enough to lift the stone.

When he had finished, Dan bent down. His hands went deep into the water, so that no one could observe the yellow substance on them. His huge arms bent around the stone, and he sank to his haunches in the water, giving his back and legs the greatest freedom for a straight lift from the ground.

He wore a cloth shirt, and as his muscles bunched around the neck and shoulders, the cloth split; but Dan paid no attention to this. For a few seconds his body was still, as if it were bound to the stone. Then there was a small shiver of the water, and his back straightened slightly. His great legs, spread apart, seemed to be driving into the bottom, as if the rock would force him down into the water rather than relinquish its hold on its ancient resting place.

An instant later the big Negro's hands showed above the water. His nails, like yellow claws against the blackness of his flesh, appeared to bite into the stone. For a moment the hands seemed to slip; but then they clamped harder against the stone and the mighty muscles of his back and shoulders leaped into full relief against the glistening blackness of his skin. A groan from his stretched lips, audible on the bank of the river, seemed to melt into a single gasp from the assembled Indians.

No one spoke, however, as the great stone rose slowly from the surface until light was visible under its dripping underside.

It was known to everyone in the village that not in the memory of any Beaver had that stone been lifted from the water. It was enough to move it; this alone marked a Beaver brave as a man of mighty strength. But now it had been lifted clear of the water!

Dan let the stone slip slowly back into the water, so that it rested on its former bed. Then he straightened up and looked across the few feet of water. Komaxala spoke:

"The son of the black spirit has moved the stone," he said,

in slow, measured words. "But it has gone back again. Perhaps its power is greater than that of the black spirit!"

Dan had been on the point of telling the Indians how God had enabled him to lift the stone. But now he stared at Komaxala, and for the first time he understood the motives of the Beaver chief.

"Oh, Jesus," he muttered. "Give Dan strength to haul this damn stone . . . amen!"

Again he stooped over, and this time the stone seemed to come up more easily. Dan's back straightened slowly, until the stone again was clear of the water. The cords of his neck stood out like thongs, and his black face gleamed against the whiteness of the river. His thick lips were drawn across his white teeth in a grimace that was like a snarl.

Slowly his back straightened, until he was standing erect, the stone a good three hands' breadth out of the water. Then he shifted one foot enough to throw his weight on it, and carefully dragged the other foot a few inches across the bottom. The strain on his arms and back was beginning to show clearly in the bunched coils of muscles under his skin, now exposed by the ripping of his shirt across the back.

He sucked air into his lungs with sudden, sobbing gasps; but inch by inch the stone moved across the water. When it was a full length away, Dan stopped. His knees bent slowly and the stone settled back into a new resting place.

As he walked ashore, he remembered to rub his hands along the sides of his leather pants; and although they left a yellow stain, none of the Indians paid any attention to this. They were watching the shambling black giant with undisguised awe.

Dan walked past Komaxala to join Thela. He took her hand in his and led her up the bank toward his tent. Komaxala lifted his hand, and by this gesture indicated that the festival should proceed as if nothing unusual had happened.

CHAPTER SIXTEEN

For many hours Dan lay in his hut, on one of the blankets Thela had brought from Komaxala's tent. His mind at first swam in a sea of exhaustion. His eyes were closed and his great body lay still except for the swelling of his chest when he breathed. Finally the strength, which seemed to have been drained from his limbs, began to pour into his body again. He opened his eyes and stared at his two silent companions.

When he was sufficiently recovered, he sat up. Thela crouched at one side of the hut, with Gnanisk close beside her; her dark eyes looked steadily at him. The two had been watching him throughout the time he lay recovering from the ordeal in the water.

Now he arose with a grunt and said:

"We gonna go upriver for some bullets." He paused for a moment. "We ain't goin' to Fort St. John," he said. "We gonna go to a tradin' post up the river that comes into this lake. We kin travel most of the way by canoe. . . ."

Thela nodded. It was not for her to question the wisdom of her new mate's decision. Dan studied her face closely to see if she had any clue to his real reason for the change of destination. Dan intended to give as his reason the fact that they could go by canoe, with a few portages, the entire distance in this direction; whereas he would have to cross several mountains to reach Fort St. John. This, however, was not his real reason . . . He still feared the white miners, despite Donald Ross' note, and he had no desire to have any Beaver, least of all Thela, know this.

Late that day Dan went into the hut of Komaxala and made his plans known to the chief. It was arranged that the Beavers would provide a canoe and a quantity of skins for trading. Dan indicated that he would also need followers to help him up the rough waterfalls on the upper river.

Komaxala, studying the face of the black man, knew that Dan would never be bound by the laws of the tribe; he would never take instructions from the chief. His victories, with his rifle and with the stone in the lake, were such that his sense of growing importance would overcome every other consideration. He knew this; yet he could not betray his black friend. It would be a fortunate thing for the Beaver tribe if Dan did not return.

"You may take those who will follow you," he said. "When you return with the profits of your journey, there will be a great feast."

Dan selected as his followers three people besides Gnanisk and, of course, Thela. These were Kichsibu, Kwolsit and Tyentegen. Kichsibu, the friend of his blind Indian slave; the futile and unlucky Kwolsit; and the disinherited warrior, Tyentegen, the miserable husband of fat Sagafewah. These were the loyal and the disinherited members of the tribe; and these he wanted as his followers.

The first two had no difficulty making up their minds to join the expedition. Kichsibu was young and glad of the opportunity to go with his blind friend; and Kwolsit's eyes shone with joy when, his selection was made known; but poor Tyentegen faced a different problem—the torment of announcing the news to his wife!

The one-time warrior who now carried his wife's burdens, cooked for her and performed menial chores about their home, went alone into the hut to break the news to her. Immediately there was a sound of screaming and the noise of broken pottery. Dan plunged into the tent and dragged Tyentegen bodily from his house. Sagafewah, the Sunrise, came waddling after them, but when she saw Dan, towering and dark, she stopped and contented herself with consigning Tyentegen and all his evil ancestors, whom she described in detail, one by one, to the land of poor hunting and starving spirits.

Dan quickly set about preparing for the trip. Thela brought such things as they should take with them and stowed them in the canoe, and beaver skins were brought down and piled into the center as ballast. Bedodid also came down to the edge of the lake to help her daughter, giving her some sinew for thread and a pair of scissors that had been acquired by her father many years before. While they were loading the canoe, a yell was heard from the direction of Tyentegen's tent, and the fat Sagafewah came sprawling through the door, turned and deposited her huge rump on the wet ground, thus effectively blocking the door.

Tyentegen's figure was discerned through the door flap; and he was completely naked. Old Sagafewah had taken his clothes, and was sitting on them.

Dan lumbered up the hill and tried to push Sagafewah away from the entrance, but she was as firm as the rock in the lake. She bent her head forward and uttered screaming imprecations against Dan and his entire expedition. At the same time she shook her pudgy finger at Tyentegen, who peered miserably from the doorway.

"Stay in there, you good-for-nothing son of a sick dog!" she screamed. "You would leave your poor wife to become sick with starving—while you go off with this black demon! Oh, no! You do not go alone—not without your wife! Do you hear that?"

The notion of Sagafewah as one of the passengers in the canoe was so startling that Dan merely gaped at her. The vision of her immense bulk, bulging over the gunwales of the bark hull, struck his imagination with such force that for the moment he was speechless.

Sagafewah, however, never lost her power of speech. She continued to spout her opinions of Dan and her husband, and to expatiate upon the miseries of a deserted wife. Meanwhile a crowd gathered, including both men and women, and they were grinning and shouting advice to Sagafewah. She maintained her position on the ground without moving her lower torso, merely waving her heavy arms and revolving her head

194

on the thick cushion of her neck as she addressed her remarks to all who listened.

Dan listened only for a short time. Then he stepped over the woman, and disappeared into the tent. In a few seconds, while even Sagafewah stared dumbfounded, he came out and with one step cleared the obstacle at the doorway. Across his shoulder was the struggling form of Tyentegen, as naked as the day he was born, although in a state of consternation such as few newborn babies display.

The crowd followed Dan down to the beach, where he unceremoniously dumped his kicking burden on the ground. He had grabbed a handful of Tyentegen's clothes, and the old Indian quickly pulled on his pants and shirt.

While Sagafewah continued to squall from the deserted battlefield in front of her hut, the other Indians quickly helped the voyagers complete the loading. There seemed to be a new friendliness among them as they helped Dan make ready to leave the village. In a short time the canoe was headed out into the lake. Dan, sitting in the stern, looked neither to the right nor left, but stared straight ahead, directing the efforts of his paddlers by gestures of his hand. It was his first command, and he intended to make the most of it. It was such a crew as few chiefs have commanded, among the Beavers or anywhere else: a blind boy, a mute woman, an unlucky hunter, and a henpecked husband. Save for Kichsibu and Dan himself, there was not a sound person in the party. But it was Dan's first moment of glory as a chief.

For the first few days progress was slow. The four male members of Dan's crew did the paddling. Thela sat in the center of the canoe and Dan himself rode pompously in the stern, surveying the shoreline as if it were all part of his domain, guiding the canoe with a paddle and exhorting his oarsmen with a rhythmic lifting of his hand.

At times Dan used the paddle to drive the canoe forward, more to relieve the monotony of his motionless position than anything else. But he quickly realized that this was menial work for a chief, and he spent most of his time gazing over the heads of his working crew and using the paddle as a rudder.

The lake was long but shallow in many places; and only the cunning of Kwolsit, who paddled in the bow, on the lookout for hidden rocks, saved them from splitting the canoe on a submerged ledge or a half-rotted branch of a tree. Both Kwolsit and Tyentegen knew how to take advantage of drifts of current and backwaters where the current would reverse the flow of the river on the upper end of the lake. And they quickly learned to convey their suggestions to Dan with diplomacy and tact. At first Dan arbitrarily decided on the direction to steer, exercising his unlimited authority; but after a few incidents in which they narrowly missed ramming a hidden rock or a submerged tree, he permitted himself to be guided by words shouted from the forward end of the canoe.

Once a black bear was sighted near the bank, and they beached the canoe. Kwolsit and Tyentegen took their muzzle-loaders ashore to stalk the bear. Dan, having no bullets for his rifle, sat down on the beach beside the canoe and watched the hunt. Gnanisk, following the beach with the aid of his stick, and Kichsibu, turning inland, converged behind the bear and made enough noise so that it started forward toward the two hunters.

Tyentegen, whose cunning in the forest was far greater than his courage at home, moved silently among the trees. When the bear reached a place within range of Tyentegen's short muzzle-loader, he fired, but the bear continued to waddle with uninterrupted calm down to the edge of the lake where it drank leisurely. Then it turned and ambled back into the woods. Kichsibu shouted in an effort to turn the bear back, but it wandered off in another direction and disappeared into the forest.

There was a sound of a single shot, and shortly afterward Kwolsit, who had gone into the woods, came out, his face plainly showing that he had not made a kill. His gun had missed fire, he explained. Dan examined the firing chamber while Kwolsit stood ruefully at one side, once again feeling the agony of failure in his heart.

Dan knew what was in the mind of each of them: Had there been any bullets for Dan's rifle, he would have dropped the bear at the first shot. This notion pleased him, and he decided to use this opportunity to explain to his crew the power of Jesus in matters of this sort.

"After we get to the trader's post, yo' is all gonna be baptize," he announced. "When yo' is baptize, yo' is the child'n of God. We gonna sing some hymns and yo' all will have white shirts for baptizin', like we done in Georgia where I come f'om."

Thela listened to him, her eyes glowing as she watched the expression of his face. Something in the low voice of the giant Negro, blending with the undertones of the forest, was like a song in the air. Dan stood above the rest, his head thrust forward as he explained earnestly the reason for the rite of baptism. None of the Indians understood what he was talking about, but each in his way understood the feelings of this man. Each was now bound to him by a peculiar tie, and each understood the quality and the enduring strength of that tie.

Later Thela made a bonfire and cleared a sleeping place on the beach; and after collecting a few branches along the beach, she went into the forest for more wood. Dan saw her going and shouted after her, but Thela by a sign indicated she was gathering wood.

"Yo' let somebody else get that wood!" Dan shouted. Gnanisk, standing beside him, spoke in a low voice, explaining that wood-gathering was the work of women.

"No!" Dan shouted, this time in a louder voice. "She ain't gonna get wood! That girl is my woman—Dan'l Williams' woman! Yo' understand that—yo' damn red heathen!" He glared at the Indians.

Kwolsit and Tyentegen said nothing; but Kichsibu, being the junior member of the crew, looked at the expression of anger on Dan's face and turned and ran into the forest. He collected Thela's bundle of wood and brought it back, not daring to look at the faces of the other Indians, since this was a moment of shame for him.

Dan sat sullenly by the fire; and when he looked at anyone, there was smouldering anger in his eyes. The two old men, Tyentegen and Kwolsit, munched their food silently, now and then stealing a careful look at the sullen face of the Negro who had now become their chief.

Finally Dan stood up before the fire, and shaking off the sullen anger that had possessed him, he fished in his shirt for his Bible.

"Each night yo' gotta lissen to some words of God," he announced. "In this forest God is strong, jes' like he is strong in the fields an' on the oceans . . . God is yo' light an' salvation, an' when yo' is baptize, yo' will die in the bosom of the Lord!"

Only Thela and Gnanisk listened carefully, their faces turned toward him. The other three Indians sat in silence, gazing at the ground or at the embers of the fire. They understood neither God, nor baptism, nor Dan.

The fall season had come over the land, and the meadows that lay in the long valley rose on either side of the river into the forested hills. The slopes of the lower hills were brown with parched grass, spotted with reddish patches of berries. As they moved slowly up the river, the land converged into sharper gorges, where waterfalls and portages impeded their travel. The little expedition beached the canoe each night, and the two old men sat by the campfire while the boys caught rabbits in snares. These were broiled over the fire and eaten with berries and honey. They saw many bears, but none was close enough to be within range of the guns of Tyentegen and Kwolsit. And so, day by day, they made their way higher into the valley where the trading post of Jacques Pardonet was located.

It was late in the evening when they rounded a bend in the river, and found the landing place of the trading post. There were several Indians at the landing, but none was of the Beaver tribe of Komaxala. As the canoe moved into shore, the Indians raised their hands in salute, and Dan acknowledged this with a regal wave of his hand.

The Indians on shore seemed to know who he was; and since they all knew Kwolsit and Tyentegen, it was not long before Dan's crew was established ashore and the Indians were exchanging tales with each other. Only the Indian women stayed back. They had seen Thela, and knew she was the daughter of a chief, and a widow . . . Yet she seemed to have married again, which was a strange thing among the Beavers, since the period of her solitude had not passed. Many of the women whispered these things as the procession of visitors passed up from the landing to the trader's house.

Thela followed Dan silently, paying no attention to the babbling of the women. Dan had given orders to Kwolsit and Tyentegen to unload the canoe, and now he walked toward the trading post of Jacques Pardonet. One of the Indians raised his hand, and approached Dan. He explained in the Beaver language that the trader was not home, having gone on an expedition with many miners over the mountains to the west.

He said he was Wandering Moose, chief of his tribe, and he had gone into the trading post only once since the French trader left. He had taken only such powder and ammunition as he needed, leaving skins for these. Since he was the chief of this region, he had the right to enter any house built in his tribal domain; but no one else had such a right.

Dan listened to the Indian; then he explained that he was also a chief, with powerful medicine. He was a free man who had only one person in the world who could tell him what to do, and that was Queen Victoria.

Wandering Moose nodded. He had heard of the great black man, whose gun spoke so straight that it could kill a bear a day's walk away; and he added that there was another black man who had traveled with Jacques Pardonet and the miners.

"Tha's Joe!" Dan exclaimed. "Yo' done seen Joe!"

"This black man is not a chief like yourself," Wandering

199

Moose said. "He carried water, which is work for women, and he cooks at the camp of the white men!"

The knowledge that Joe was with the miners as a handyman was both cheering and disturbing to Dan. He was glad his friend was alive; but in his new eminence as a chief, Dan did not like to be reminded of his former position among the miners of Fort St. John.

"Yo' done heard about me shootin' them white folks?" Dan asked.

Wandering Moose said nothing. It was not wise to mingle in the curious affairs of white people, or of black people for that matter. He waved his hand toward the trader's house, and suggested that Dan might do as he had done—cut away the moose-skin window and crawl into the shack. Dan shook his head.

"Dan is goin' through the door," he said abruptly; but for the rest of the day he said nothing more about this, deciding that it was something to be considered carefully. In the land of the traders, breaking into a trading post was worse than killing a man. It was the only unforgivable offense.

That night, as he lay rolled in his blanket by the fire, Dan thought about this problem. He had spoken too quickly about going into the trader's house; that much was certain. It would have been better to have said nothing, remaining outside until Jacques Pardonet's return.

On the other hand, there was a matter of pride to be considered. Wandering Moose had gone into the house, even though it was by way of the window. Was Dan to be regarded as less of a chief? He had said he would go in through the door, and in he must go!

Suddenly it struck him that he had a kind of medicine that none of the Beavers possessed. He could write! It was not easy for him to write, and he had never been able to figure out why some letters were large and others small. But since he could read words in the Bible, he could also write them. He would write a letter to Jacques Pardonet, explaining why he had entered the post to trade! This was medicine that no Indian could match! It would give him a reputation for knowing secret signs, communicating his thoughts and wishes by these signs on paper . . . This would increase his fame, indeed!

Writing the note was not easy. The next morning Dan went boldly into the trading post, but before he looked at the articles for which he intended to trade his beaver skins, he sat down at a table and with a pencil he found in a rack above the table, he laboriously scrawled this note:

DANieL WiLLiAMS by yuR cARtRiS ALSo tobACCo ALSo ShuRt to GoD to BAptiSE tHESE DAM iNDians tHANK yu D. WiLLiAMS.

Dan was quite proud of the note, once he had written it; and he put it where the trader would be sure to see it when he came back. Then he began to look over the goods. There were many things he needed. As often as he saw a new article, he knew it was something he wanted. He took a knife and three hatchets as well as tobacco and ammunition; and finally he rummaged through the bolts of material until he found several rolls of white cloth.

At each new acquisition, Dan would lay out several skins; when the supply of skins began to thin out, he took back several so he could pay them out again for other supplies. By this means he was able to achieve a perfect balance between the supply of skins and the articles for which he traded. For example, he would take twenty cartridges out of a box, and hang up one beaver skin. Then, when he decided he needed more cartridges, he took one of the skins he had allocated for white cloth, and hung this on a hook over the cartridges. It would be all the same to the trader, he decided, because even if he got one less skin for the cloth, he got one more for the cartridges.

By this simple method of accounting, Dan was able to collect all the articles he wanted and pay for them. Thela stood by, watching him with undisguised admiration. Dan counted carefully at first, but he soon became confused with his figures, and in the end he decided that all the articles not covered by beaver skins might be considered as a trading gift anyway . . . And there was the added fact that Jacques Pardonet was on Dan's side of God, and would undoubtedly be happy to furnish white cloth for baptizing without charge.

When he had finished trading, he was so satisfied with what had been done that he decided to write another message. Lacking any paper, he wrote on a board:

DANieL WiLLiAMS HeeR WiLL cuM AGiN

Dan had placed the paper giving the details of his trading transactions on the table, and the board he nailed to the door. It did not occur to him that a wind, blowing through rents in the moose-skin window, might blow the paper away, leaving only the message on the board to advise the trader, in somewhat ominous language, of Dan Williams' visit, and of his intention to "come again."

Dan closed the door, and showed the Beaver chief, Wandering Moose, the words he had written. This, he explained, was the way white men and black men behaved, communicating with each other by written signs. Wandering Moose stared at the message in wonder; he had seen the amount of goods Dan had obtained for a few ill-assorted beaver skins, and never in his experience with white traders had he seen so few skins traded for so many articles.

Dan had not been quite sure of his counting methods, so he informed Chief Wandering Moose that in the event there were any unequal benefits in the trade, he would talk this over with Jacques Pardonet when the trader returned; and at any rate, those who could read the sign would not be in doubt that some trading had taken place.

The following day, before the sun was up, Dan ordered his crew to load the canoe for the trip back to the Beaver village. There were boxes of tea and salt and sugar, enough ammunition to last all winter, and new knives and hatchets. In the center of the canoe, where the beaver pelts had been stowed, there were several bolts of white cloth, with Thela proudly

202

riding on them. It was early dawn, and few of the Indians of Chief Wandering Moose's tribe were awake when Dan's canoe was pushed out into the river and headed downstream again.

Dan remembered to kneel down just before they left and pray to God and Jesus, giving thanks for the great store of goods they had been able to obtain from the Frenchman's trading post. After that he felt better satisfied, as if this prayer had in a sense eradicated any minor imperfections in the trading; and Thela and Gnanisk both understood, one from the repose of Dan's face and the other from the sound of his voice, that he was again at peace with the world.

Thela always watched Dan when he prayed. He held his clasped hands in front of his face, and he often prayed aloud so the effect would be felt not only in heaven, where the prayers were directed, but also among the Indians who listened. Unfortunately, no one except Dan, who often repeated the messages, knew what God said in reply, so Thela's only source of this knowledge was from Dan's face.

Now she watched him, turning from time to time to look back at him. She saw from the smooth, high glow of his black face that he had no troubles, and his eyes, dark and shining, looked steadily downriver, and now and then turned toward the sky.

Dan was planning, as they floated swiftly downstream, something that would establish his place among the Beavers! He looked now and then at the folds of white cloth upon which Thela sat, and his thoughts glowed with the promise of future devotion to the glory of God.

These thoughts were so pleasing that he began to sing hymns, in his strong, melodious voice. After a while he encouraged the others to join him, teaching them the words as well as he could. In the shadow of night, as the canoe floated down toward the Beaver village, there arose in the evening air a strange mixture of Christian hymns, with words and music as intelligible to the lynxes and wolverines scuttling through the forest along the shore as they would have been to Christians of other lands.

CHAPTER SEVENTEEN

Several Indians stood on the beach as Dan's well-laden canoe curved in from the middle of the lake toward the shore. Komaxala was not among them, although he had been informed many hours before that the black visitor's canoe had been sighted on the river above the lake. He sat in his tent, seeking from the spirits of nature above and around him some insight into the most perplexing problem he had faced as a chief.

Old Ikta was dead; and the menace of his hatred of Dan and his ambition to rule the tribe had died with him. But there were others among the Beavers who would think as Ikta thought . . . This was a matter that must be considered carefully and wisely by the chief. He had hoped, of course, that Dan would continue on his voyage, without the protection of many warriors. There was always the possibility that other tribes might fall upon the little party and destroy them. This had not happened; and the son of the black spirit once again was his guest.

After a while, Komaxala rose from the blanket upon which he had been sitting and walked down to the beach. Here a strange spectacle confronted him. The male members of Dan's crew were standing on the beach, lined up beside the canoe. And all were wearing long white robes, made of cotton cloth!

One of the Beaver warriors, Tumike, who had recently returned from an absence of more than two years—during which he had traveled all the way to the great sea which spread itself to the southward of the big forests—explained to Komaxala the purpose of these strange doings.

"It is a custom of the white men, in their own places of living, to dress in such a fashion," he said. "Not only women but the braves also dress in this way when they are ready to speak to the Great Spirit."

Komaxala nodded. He knew vaguely of such practices. It was the custom of white men constantly to wrap themselves in white cloth. They even wrapped the bodies of those who died from sickness in such clothing, and buried them in boxes . . . Perhaps Dan was about to slay his crew! Komaxala began to watch the affair. Dan saw him and came forward, his coarse face split in a wide grin. He held out his hand and the chief gravely took it.

"We gonna baptize these folks in the light of God, an' in the bosom of Jesus Christ!" he said. "Yo' all wanna join in?"

Komaxala shook his head; and still he did not smile. He saw that Dan carried the tattered book in his hand from which he had produced the magic words that brought life back to his daughter. The chief was curious; and also he was strangely disturbed. These were new and strange events; and there could be evil in them.

Dan went briskly about the business of baptizing his crew. The fact that his Bible was pretty well torn, and some of the pages stuck together, was an obstruction to the ceremony he was about to conduct; but since the Indians would never know the difference, he decided to read what he could and try to remember the rest. The white cloth, however, was an inspiration; it would compensate for any other defects in the ceremony.

Tumike, who acquired an air of authority from the fact that he was the only person in the village except Dan who knew what the ceremony of baptism was designed for, explained to Komaxala what was about to happen. He had lived for many moons with the white people, and he had seen a medicine man of the white tribe who was reported to be a man in winter and a woman in the summer, perform such ceremonies, dressing Indians of the lower countries in white garments and throwing water at them.

Komaxala listened in grave silence. Dan, meanwhile, had assembled his group of four men at the edge of the river. They appeared strangely imposing in the white robes, which were fastened by pins Dan had taken from Jacques Pardonet's stores; even Komaxala was impressed by the sight.

Dan stood before them and in a voice that rang across the lake in wild echoes of sound, he roared out several hymns, singing them in succession so that the effect would not be lost upon the four candidates for baptism. In a country where everyone was used to the ritual of baptism, the hymns could have been sung in a more orderly way; but Dan knew he could not hope to hold the attention of his candidates through any protracted periods of silence, so he kept on singing continuously for perhaps ten minutes.

Then he ordered them to walk into the water. He stood on the beach and sang while the four Indians walked out until the water was up to their waists.

Dan's singing was interrupted by an even more impelling voice. Sagafewah, the fat Sunrise of Tyentegen, stood on the beach, her fists on her massive hips, and roared to her mate to come ashore.

Tyentegen looked at her from the water, torn between two schools of thought. Dan had offered him double the amount of tobacco he would normally have given him as an inducement to be baptized; and Tyentegen was a man who enjoyed smoking. But Sagafewah had negative inducements of another kind, and they were not pleasant to think about. She would be sure to strike him when he was not expecting it; and she would throw cooking utensils at him unless he obeyed her.

He looked helplessly first at Dan and then at his spouse. Dan had explained that the baptism would not be complete until some message of God, such as a pigeon, appeared in the sky. No bird had appeared; and Tyentegen was afraid he would not receive the extra allocation of tobacco if he broke ranks too soon.

Finally he shouted at his wife, "The black chief has promised much tobacco—you will have it for yourself!"

Sagafewah screamed that she was not in a mood for smoking; and she waved a stick to indicate what her mood was at the moment.

Dan turned toward her.

"Woman!" he roared. "Yo' either gets the hell outa here and lets me baptize these child'en in the mercy of the Lord, or I'll drag yo' out into the water with the rest of 'em . . . This here is a holy matter, an' the will of God is bein' done, amen!"

Sagafewah understood little of what Dan said; but she noted from Tyentegen's indecision that he was weakening, so she poured forth a torrent of scolding abuse, paying no attention to Dan. Finally, with a despairing glance in Dan's direction, Tyentegen began wading ashore.

Dan uttered a loud shout, and jumped into the water, striding toward the fleeting candidate. He grabbed Tyentegen around the waist and, before Tyentegen had time to put up any resistance, accomplished a complete baptism by immersion. Tyentegen came up sputtering. His Christian robe was wrapped around the upper part of his body, including his face, and the nether portions were without adornment of any kind.

The Indians lined up on the beach, laughing at Tyentegen, and this encouraged Sagafewah to go in after him. She pulled her red flannel skirt, which came only to her knees, up against her waist and with her huge thighs exposed to the gaze of the crowd, waddled into the water.

Dan was trying to unwrap the baptismal cloth from Tyentegen's head, and the old Indian was struggling to breathe through the swath, which was now entangled around his shoulders. Sagafewah grabbed one end of the robe and began to pull; Tyentegen spun slowly, like a top, until he lost his balance and plunged in for his second baptismal immersion of the afternoon.

The other candidates had crowded closer to see what was happening; and they broke into laughter, even the blind Gnanisk laughing for the first time in weeks, although he understood only from Kichsibu what was going on.

Sagafewah tore the last shred of the white cloth from her trembling mate, and with a tremendous slap on the portion

207

of his bare exterior that seemed most likely to accelerate him, she sent him stumbling toward the shore.

Dan watched the dissolution of his baptismal ceremonies with growing concern. He looked at Sagafewah, her fat face congealed with frozen hatred; suddenly he reached out with a long black arm, and caught her by the fat folds of her neck. With a quick heave, he sent the old woman plunging into the water.

"Yo' ain't fit for baptizin'," he roared, "but yo' all shore as hell gonna get wet!"

Sagafewah came up, spluttering with rage but too choked to make any intelligible noise; and after a glance at Dan's glowering face, she turned and headed for shore. She paid no attention to the other Indians, but started up the slope after Tyentegen, who was already well on the way to his tent.

Dan turned to the three in the water, who now stood in shivering uncertainty, holding the clammy folds of their white robes around them. He held up his hand and began to sing. He indicated by the pumping of his hands that they should join with him, singing the hymns he had tried to teach them on the trip downriver.

The singing was of mixed quality and volume. Dan finally stopped, and grabbing old Kwolsit around the waist, he quickly upended him. Kwolsit came up sputtering.

"Did yo' see the white pigeon?" Dan shouted. Kwolsit dismally shook his head. Dan seized him again, and this time when Kwolsit came up, spewing water from his mouth, he had no hesitation about agreeing to Dan's inquiry about the white pigeon.

Kichsibu took the immersion quickly and gracefully, swimming up under his own power; and when Dan asked him about seeing the white pigeon, he agreed the first time.

"Hallelujah!" Dan roared. "Yo' is saved f'om sin!"

Gnanisk was immersed, but since the matter of seeing the white pigeon was somewhat academic with him, Dan omitted this inquiry. Turning to the crowd on the beach, he explained that all except Tyentegen—who would be taken care of later—

had now been baptized, and were cleansed in the eyes of God. All their sins had been washed away, and it was up to them to stay clean—which he doubted they would do, since nobody ever stayed completely clean from sin. This ceremony gave them a better chance than most people, however; then Dan explained that any other Beavers might have the same treatment if they wished.

Dan led his small flock back to his hut, where they crouched in wet robes while he made tea. A few of the other Indians followed, but most went to their own huts, the women to work and the men to sleep. Dan brought out tobacco and tea that he had gotten from Jacques Pardonet's stores and passed them around. Then he sent word to the chief that the stores should be divided among all the Beavers in the village—since he had used the skins of the Beaver tribe to make his "trade" with the absent trader.

Tumike arrived with Komaxala. He carried a gun exactly like Dan's, and he held the weapon rather ostentatiously in front of him.

Dan stared at the gun. It was not polished, however, as his own gun was polished; and it was possible that Tumike had gotten an old gun in a trade with a white man and probably did not know how to care for it or use it.

"How she shoot?" he asked.

Tumike looked at Dan with dislike in his eyes.

"The black guest must know," he said. "It is like your own gun. It has not happened that I have ever shot at an animal that did not die. My gun shoots straighter than any other gun!"

Dan grunted. Komaxala, watching the Negro with shrewd eyes, permitted Tumike to speak, an unusual privilege. It was also unusual for an Indian to brag . . . and Dan, even in the uncertainty of his own thoughts, was aware that the conduct of this new Beaver was unusual.

"Yo' like to bet on that?" Dan asked. Tumike nodded, and said:

"You have many bullets for your gun. I have bullets for mine.

Each will bet the bullets for his gun, and the one that shoots best will have all the bullets."

Dan looked at Komaxala, but the face of the chief was expressionless. It struck Dan that if he lost all the bullets for his gun, he would be as badly off as he was before he entered the trading post of Jacques Pardonet. But he knew that if he refused to make the bet with Tumike, he would be shamed before all the Beavers—and this would be worse than having no bullets.

It was agreed that they should shoot at each other's pipe— so that the loser would lose not only his bullets but the enjoyment of smoking. The two contestants went down to the beach, and the pipes were set on a branch. Before they shot, however, a raven landed on a branch of the tree where the pipes had been placed, and Dan called out to Tumike:

"Shoot the bird! Shoot the bird!"

Tumike placed the stock of the gun against his cheek, aimed and fired. The bird did not move. Dan quickly raised his gun and without appearing to take aim, fired. The bird dropped off the branch, its head torn from its body.

He looked at Komaxala, and the wooden face of the chief did not betray any of his thoughts. But he turned away and no longer seemed concerned with the contest.

When the shooting was over, and Dan had won all of Tumike's bullets, he walked over to Komaxala. His heavy brows were drawn into a frown, and he placed a hand on the arm of the chief.

"Yo' wanted him to win Dan's bullets," he said. "Why yo' wan' that? Is it maybe 'cause yo' don' like Dan no mo'?"

Komaxala looked at the black man, who stood several inches taller than the Indian, who was a tall man for his tribe. His gaze was direct, and finally he said:

"If your bullets had been given to Tumike, you would have had to leave this village again . . . It is better that you go, son of the black spirit. My people are not your people. You speak of different spirits, and you follow the laws of the white man—not the laws of our people. You have the heart of a warrior and a child, but your brain is not that of an Indian."

Dan gazed at the chief with a troubled face. He had lived in the home of the Beavers for many months, and his position as a great hunter was known to all of them . . . Yet Komaxala was now asking him to leave!

The chief laid his hand upon the black man's shoulder.

"If you leave, my daughter will go with you . . . She speaks to no one, except those who are dead. Yet she will be your mate. She will bear your sons—the sons of a great warrior of the black people, and a warrior of the Beaver people."

A weight seemed to have settled on Dan's heart. He looked at the chief, and shook his head.

"I guess Dan ain't no chief," he said. "Dan ain't no hunter— Dan ain't nobody! Jes' a damn fool nigger. . . ."

Dan went back to his hut. He did not speak to Thela, although she stood waiting for him, her eyes shining with a glow that appeared only when she looked at him. When she observed that he would not speak, she lowered her eyes and walked into the hut, following after him. She sat motionless for a long time, looking at the huge form of the Negro, his head hunched forward, his massive jaw cupped in his big black hands. He looked like a mighty mold of stone, carved by an artist of perfect skill, as he sat thinking, silent and still in the midst of his brooding thoughts.

Finally he raised his eyes and looked at Thela.

"We goin' some place else to live," he announced. "Yo' gotta begin packin' up our stuff." He looked around the hut—at the blankets hung neatly on the wall, the rifle and fishing pole, the clean pots of iron and baked clay. This hut had become his home, and he was loath to leave it . . . Yet he knew that what Komaxala had said was true: the Indians of the Beaver tribe did not like him. He was not one of them. He was a great hunter, yet no one spoke of his skill. He had brought back the daughter of the chief from death, by his prayers to God . . . yet no one had spoken words of gratitude, and there were those who did not like him because of this.

He would take Thela and Gnanisk into the mountains, and

Kwolsit and Tyentegen might come if they wished. He would set up his house, and teach his small flock the words of God, which he would read from his Bible. This notion gave Dan a renewed feeling of his own importance, cheering him to some extent. He quickly forgot the hurt that lay like a weight upon his heart, and began to think of the new life he would find in the forest, teaching his flock.

Within a short time Thela had gathered together their possessions, including many of the things they had brought down from Jacques Pardonet's trading store. Komaxala said little to Dan during the days before he left, but he often stood before his tent and looked down toward the hut where Dan and Thela lived. When they had piled the belongings they wished to take beside the canoe on the beach, the chief came down with Bedodid to speak a few words of farewell to his daughter and to his black friend.

"When you have hunted in the woods, and killed moose and deer for your food and for the clothes that will cover you, perhaps you will come back to this village and bring warmth to an old man's heart," he said, sententiously. Dan listened to his words, knowing that they were without meaning.

He had lived as a free man for many years in the Peace River country; yet the only place where he had been treated as a free man was in the village of the Beavers. Among the miners at Fort St. John, and with the traders of the Hudson's Bay Company, he had not been a free man. He had been given the meanest and dirtiest work in the camp, and men had shot at him—and tried to hunt him down and kill him because he had shot back and killed white men.

Yet there was a strange difference: among the Beavers he was respected as a hunter, but he was not liked; whereas among the white men of Fort St. John and Fort Vermilion he had been treated with scorn and contempt, but no one had hated him. This was a point that puzzled Dan; and he found in the faces of the Indians around him no answer to his question.

Dan knew that if his stock of bullets was gone, he would be useless as a hunter, since he was not a man to put up traps. .

212

He prayed to God as often as he thought about it; yet he could not see how God could help him if he had no bullets to shoot in his gun.

These thoughts bewildered him as he pushed out into the lake, intending to cross it and cache his canoe at the lower end, and then travel into the mountains with Thela and the blind Gnanisk. For the first time in many months Dan was a very sorrowful man.

Dan had been gone from the village with his small party for perhaps two weeks when Jacques Pardonet arrived. He had come downriver from his trading post, with two Indian helpers, and crossed the lake in his canoe. It was easy to see that he was not in a pleasant mood. He drove his birchbark canoe hard against the beach, and without speaking a word, climbed out. His short, wide body was clothed in dark leather, and he wore a fur hat, set squarely on his round, bulletlike head. He scarcely looked at any of the Beaver braves, but settled his eyes on the house of the chief.

When Komaxala came down to greet him—appearing to have just learned of his arrival, although he had known for hours that the squat French trader was on his way toward the Beaver village—the chief held up his hand in greeting.

Jacques did not respond to the gesture. He stared at Komaxala with his black eyes, and asked:

"Where is that God-damn nigger?"

This was unusual talk for the trader. He seldom spoke directly, which was a custom with people of his race and calling. Komaxala shook his head, saying nothing.

Trader Jacques launched into a tirade of language, part Beaver and part English and part French. No one understood exactly what he was saying, but the general meaning was clear: He had come back to his trading post before the winter ice formed, having led a group of miners to the high waterfalls in the Rocky Mountain passes. This was many days' travel, and he had left them to make their way over the passes to the Fraser River. What had happened to them since he did not know, and he didn't give a damn. What he wanted to know

213

was the whereabouts of that "God-damn nigger."

He had journeyed back to his trading post and found chaos. His goods had been taken, with a few scrawny beaver pelts left as an insult to his profession; and a note had been written on a board which was both insulting and threatening.

What Jacques Pardonet wanted to know was this: How could a man live in a country as long as he had, bargaining fairly with the Indians, bringing goods such as knives and needles that they could not get elsewhere—how could such a fair-minded man survive in a land of burglars and thieves?

He was not the man to put up with anything like this! He had not waited until the next day, or even the next hour. He had found out immediately who entered his trading post and looted his stocks; and he had climbed into his canoe almost immediately and started downriver.

Now he wanted to know—what was the great Beaver chief, Komaxala, going to do about it? Was trading to be done in the Beaver country in this way—that is, when the trader himself was not around? Was this the way the Beaver people maintained their honor? If so, he would spit on their honor! Jacques spit on the ground to illustrate his point.

Komaxala listened patiently. He understood nothing of the cause of this, believing Dan's story that he had used his knowledge of signs familiar to white people and black people to conclude his trading with the Frenchman. If the Frenchman did not understand those signals, this was a matter of great surprise.

The Frenchman, gesticulating wildly as he talked, shouted that it was not necessary that he read English to conduct a trading post in the Indian country. Who else read English? Not Komaxala, to be sure! Besides, he knew what the sign had said. It said Dan Williams had been there, and would come again!

Well, let him come! Jacques patted his gun to make his point clear.

The next day Kwolsit and Tyentegen, who had been with Dan on the trip, thought it might be wise to show the trader

214

certain of the spiritual results of the excursion. The black hunter had told them how gladly Jacques Pardonet would have contributed the white baptismal cloth had he known it was to be used in the service of the Lord.

The cloth was not as clean as it had been when Dan took it from the shelves of the trading post, but this was not of any concern to the two Indians. They wrapped themselves in the cloth, and strode past the Frenchman, as he sat at the door of Dan's hut—which had been given to him to use during his visit to the Beaver village—looking at Jacques with undisguised smiles.

Jacques jumped to his feet.

"Thieves!" he shouted, brandishing his fist. "It ees my cloth you have—my good cloth! *Chacon!* Peegs! You insult Jacques Pardonet!"

There was seldom much hiatus between thought and action in the life of Jacques Pardonet. In trading he could be as patient and skillful as a Syrian. He would devote much preliminary talk to the amenities, skirting around the subject of trading until he had reduced his opponent to the brink of acquiescence. He could be aggrieved, emphatic, logical, humorous, petulant, or angry, as the occasion required.

But in a matter of honor, there was no such period of deliberation. His reactions were spontaneous and instantaneous. He grabbed his gun with one hand, and started for the two Indians. They were so surprised at the suddenness of his attack that they stood still, not even trying to defend themselves.

Jacques did not use the gun. He dropped it when he was near enough, in order to make better use of his hands. With a roar, he descended upon the pair swathed in their white baptismal garb, grabbing each by the back of the neck. He brought his powerful arms together, like the pincers of a crab, and Kwolsit and Tyentegen rebounded against each other's forehead.

An Indian brave—even an old one—seldom gives expression to pain or fear. But these two were entirely unprepared for the assault. They both yelled at once.

215

Several braves were aroused from their afternoon slumbers by this noise, and they came out to see what was going on. Jacques still had the pair, one beefy hand grabbing the neck of each, and was banging their heads together like a man playing the cymbals. Both Kwolsit and Tyentegen were so paralyzed with surprise, and the numbing effect of having their heads beaten together, that they scarcely resisted, but merely bellowed each time their heads snapped back.

Komaxala came to the door of his hut and directed several braves to interfere, at least until he could determine the reason for the strange behavior of the visiting Frenchman. Jacques not only resented the interference, but he resisted it, dropping the necks of Kwolsit and Tyentegen for the moment, and turning toward the other Indians.

In a short time what had been a peaceful camp turned into a general brawl. Jacques Pardonet was an unusually powerful man, and because of his shape—squat, and built low to the ground—he was practically indestructible. None of the Indians wanted to kill a white man, since they had solemn treaties with the Queen and Her Majesty's Governors; furthermore, Jacques Pardonet was so well known it would have been difficult to dispose of his body without incurring suspicion. Komaxala had made signs to his braves that they must not kill the trader. However, it quickly became necessary for the Indians to do something to avoid injury to themselves.

The Frenchman was holding his own, and roaring like a wounded bull moose, until one of the warriors cracked him on top of the head with a club. His bellows, which could have been heard across the lake, ceased and he collapsed in the tangle of arms and legs that had been milling around him.

After some discussion, it was decided that the best thing was to take him down and put him in his canoe. It was necessary to tie his hands, since he might recover his senses at any moment and strike out again. But none of his goods was taken, except paddles. The currents in the lake would carry him to some shore farther down, where his two Indian helpers might find it possible to revive him, or at least return to their own village.

It was well known that Jacques Pardonet was a powerful man, and practically invulnerable; therefore he could not be killed, except perhaps by a bear. Since none of the Indians had tried to kill him, no one could be held responsible.

After the canoe had drifted out of sight, a big fire was built and the elders of the tribe gathered with Komaxala to smoke a pipe and discuss the situation, which might bode ill for the Beaver people.

CHAPTER EIGHTEEN

It was spring, some four years later, when a canoe worked its way slowly down the Peace River in the neighborhood of Fort St. John. In the canoe were a huge black man and an Indian woman.

Dan and Thela had come down from the mountains when the winter freeze began to break, and now they were heading downriver toward the place from which Dan had fled many years before. His great frame bowed forward as he dipped his paddle into the water, guiding the canoe toward the shore where the tumbled-down remnants of the old miners' camp lay under the slopes of bare hills that rose sharply to the south.

The Peace River flowed calmly, carrying an assortment of timbers that had drifted down from the mountains, branches that broke away from the river edge, and debris from streams higher up. It gradually descended across the wide, barren plains toward Fort Vermilion and the Slave Lakes.

Dan sang a hymn, now and then, breaking the silence that made the middle of the river as desolate as the desert. In the bow sat his mute companion; the blind Gnanisk was no longer with them. Far back in the mountains he had died; either he

217

slipped and fell into a waterfall or had leaped into it to put an end to the miserable and senseless fate that the spirits had inflicted upon him because of a sudden moment of youthful curiosity. Since Gnanisk died, Dan had not heard the sound of a human voice, except his own.

His gun lay in the canoe, empty of bullets. He had not fired it for many months; his last bullet had killed a moose early in the winter. This meat lasted for many weeks; finally, however, it gave out, and during the late winter months Dan and Thela had eaten only the meat of rabbits they were able to snare, or small animals killed with a club or a spear.

Dan's "freedom" now 'had come to an end. He had no bullets, and he could not survive without them. He must go back to Dunvegan to work as a handyman and cook: the property of a white master who would order him about and beat him when he failed to obey or when he displeased the white man. He would once more be Nigger Dan, the camp handyman. . . .

As night fell, he turned the canoe toward the northern shore and beached it. There was no one on the beach, and he looked for a place along the river to fish so that he and Thela could eat. Then he sat by the fire, closed in by the cold gloom of the night and the wind that roared down from the snow-covered Rockies. Thela sat on the other side of the fire, watching the lights and shadows upon Dan's face. He scarcely noticed her. Silence always lay between them, like the overpowering gulf of time . . . a chasm that could not be bridged unless by some circumstance they might find a way of communicating in which each could understand the other.

Dan was sleepless during the night, thinking over his life— the life of a one-time slave, who had become a great man in the woods. Suddenly he was struck by an idea: He would not go down to Dunvegan to get a job with white people! He would not go back to the life of a slave—a man who must jump out of bed at the first sound of the bell in the morning, and begin to do chores that must be finished before other men had their breakfast . . . and then eat what was left when the other men had eaten! This was not freedom! It was not the freedom of the woods and the Beaver village, where he had been a great hunter!

No . . . he would go over to Fort St. John and settle in the deserted cabin of the trader, Donald Ross, or in one of the shacks left by the miners. He remembered that Tiny had found gold there; and perhaps there was more. He was a free man! Once he had signed his name to a piece of paper which made him a "subject" of Queen Victoria. He would live as a free man at the deserted trading post. He would get bullets from traders; perhaps there were some left in abandoned cabins at the old mining camp.

Without waiting for morning, Dan quickly shook Thela, who had fallen asleep on the other side of the fire. She sat up, looking around quickly, perhaps looking for enemies who might have crept up to their camp during the night.

But Dan was laughing joyously. His thick lips parted, showing his white teeth; and he pointed across the river, where old Fort St. John lay.

"We gonna go over there!" he shouted. "Oh Glory Hallelujah! Dan gonna set up his house at ol' Fort St. John, and maybe do some tradin' an' build a church! Only one person in the worl' gonna tell Dan what to do, an' that's Queen Victoria. I gotta contrac' with the Queen——" He remembered the paper he had signed at Port Arthur many years ago; and although he had never seen the paper again, he knew it was a "contrac' " . . . At Fort St. John he would become Dan Williams, the trader—like the Hudson's Bay Company. He would be the equal of any white man!

He continued to talk, expecting no reply from Thela. She understood most of his words, and she watched with the fire in her eyes that was the only language she possessed. Now and then she raised her hands and made a sign, which he understood. But for the most part she listened silently; when Dan jumped up and ordered her to make ready to paddle across the river as soon as the sun came up behind the old camp site, she rose and began to assemble their supplies.

At daybreak they paddled across the river. Dan recognized

the old buildings of the Hudson's Bay Company; and in the place where the trading post had been, he saw some changes. New walls had been built, making a larger store. He approached the place, wondering whether Donald Ross and Banjo Mike had returned. But there was no sign of human life. The new trading post was only half finished, and the boards were weathered and old.

Dan knew that it was necessary to mark the ground at four points, sixty paces each way, where he intended to make his home; he found four sticks and paced off the required distance, driving the stakes into the ground. He had no pencil, but with the point of his knife he marked his name—D. WiLLiAMs—on each stake.

After this, he went into the half-finished house, and while Thela was arranging things in their new home, he went to sleep. He had paddled many days, and the thought of going back to Dunvegan and working for white folks again had made his body tired . . . It was some time later that he felt someone tug at his shoulder, and saw Thela standing above him.

She pointed upriver, and held up her hands. The signs she made told him that two canoes were approaching the shore.

Dan jumped to his feet, ran through the door and down to the beach, looking at the approaching canoes; suddenly he shouted.

"Banjo! It's you, Massa Banjo—Lord he'p me, if it ain't!"

Banjo Mike sat in the stern of the leading canoe, his bristling beard cracked in a grin of recognition. He jumped ashore as soon as the canoe had grounded and shook Dan's hand.

The other boat was larger—a York boat; and it was filled with several people, the leader of whom was a young man whose name was George Kennedy.

He stared at Dan, after Banjo Mike had explained his earlier relations with Dan, and then George Kennedy said shortly:

"So you're Nigger Dan, eh?"

Dan became silent. He had lived with the Indians for a long time, and he found it difficult to speak to another man in English. The times he had spoken English aloud were in moments of prayer, or excitement; and it made little difference if he did not say exactly the right words. But here was a young man who spoke English, and who looked unfavorably at him.

Banjo Mike was speaking, and suddenly Dan understood what he was saying.

George Kennedy was the new factor of the Hudson's Bay Company. He had come to take over the trading post, which was only partly finished. Dan looked up toward the house, where he had recently been sleeping. His gaze then traveled to the places where his stakes had been placed, and saw that they were still there.

When George Kennedy found that Dan already had moved his belongings into the house, he became serious.

"I'm sorry, old boy, but you'll have to move out," he said. "This place belongs to the Company."

Dan stared at the young man, and then his eyes rolled from George Kennedy to the York boat, where the men were already unloading boxes.

"I done put my stakes in the groun'," he said. "The law say tha's my place, don' it?"

"Not if you put them on the Company's ground," Kennedy said in clipped tones, biting off his words as if he regretted the necessity of using them on the huge black man. "It's the Company's house."

Banjo Mike was standing by, chewing on a splinter and grinning as he looked first at Dan and then at the trader.

"Not if you ain't been here for five years, by God!" Banjo Mike said suddenly. "An' I don't think you been here in that time." He started to figure on his fingers, and then stopped. "You ain't," he said, slowly.

Kennedy looked sharply at the red-bearded trader. He knew Banjo Mike by reputation; he had recently met him at Dunvegan, and they had come down the river together because both were headed in the same general direction. But he had no personal ties with the free trader; and he knew that every free trader desired one thing above all else: to keep the Company out of as many trading places as possible.

"Accordin' to law, Dan's got a right to that house," Banjo Mike continued, grinning at the young man. "He came here first, an' you ain't had anybody here since Ross left—an' I left with him five years ago!"

"We've had workmen," Kennedy said.

"That was a couple of months afterward. You still ain't had anybody here in five years. I think you'd better go back and talk to MacFarlane about this. He's a judge in this district, an' he ain't gonna want to break the law."

MacFarlane was the "principal man of the Company" in this area, with headquarters at Fort Vermilion. George Kennedy was young, but he was no fool. He produced a map from his boat and studied the lines. It was a blueprint, showing the location of the trading post.

Dan stared at the map. He was not used to looking at a printed map, and this one seemed to be more than ordinarily official. He shifted his eyes from the map to Kennedy. If the new factor intended to stay here, it would not be a good idea to make an enemy of him. Dan might have to work as handyman and cook, and it would be bad if the man he worked for already disliked him.

Suddenly Dan asked:

"Yo' work for Queen Victoria?"

Kennedy's sharp, smooth face betrayed little surprise. He had dealt with simple people, and he felt that he understood how to handle them. It was better to appease their simplicity, and then you had them working for you rather than against you.

"Certainly," he said. "We all work for Queen Victoria."

"Yo' got a contrac'? Her name on that paper?"

Kennedy shook his head.

"Her Majesty doesn't have time to sign all the papers," he said, patiently. "But it certainly was with her authority that this house was built."

"Ef yo' ain't got her name, yo' ain't got a contrac'," Dan said firmly. "I got a contrac' with the Queen." His voice was

222

less firm on the last statement. He wondered whether the paper he signed could be found anywhere.

Kennedy, watching Banjo Mike, recognized that the shrewd old trader might cause some difficulty in this case. It was much better to arrange the matter satisfactorily to all concerned, so he said to Dan:

"Suppose I pay you for your rights to the house . . . You can stay on the land if you want, just sell me your rights to the house."

In a short time Kennedy's helpers would have gone back to Fort Vermilion, and it would be a good idea to have this powerful Negro as a handyman.

Finally Dan said:

"Yo' give me two hundred ca'tridges, an' tobacco an' tea an' sugar—tha's two shares for me an' my squaw. You kin have the house."

Kennedy looked at Dan. It was not much trading material to assure the occupancy of the house without being molested; and he was not certain of the legal rights involved. He had heard of Dan Williams. He had killed many miners, and there was also the report that he had killed a French trader, Jacques Pardonet, whose body had been found some years ago, lying in a canoe afloat in a lake in the Beaver country. He had been killed by a blow on the head, and Dan Williams was known to have been in the vicinity about the time he was killed. It was fairly certain he had murdered the Frenchman.

On the other hand, the cost of travel back to Vermilion to ask MacFarlane what to do would be excessive, and might subject the young factor to criticism. He had orders to build the house, and a small payment to Dan Williams could be justified as a necessary expense.

"All right," he said. "I'll pay you the two hundred cartridges, and the rest of the stuff. But we want the house and all the land down to the river. We plan to build a storehouse and a landing there, and you'll have to write your name on a piece of paper so there won't be any question about it."

Dan nodded. He suddenly found himself raised to a new

peak of importance. He glanced at Thela, wishing she could understand all this; he would have to explain it to her later. She was a heathen, with no knowledge of writing, or contracts, or Queen Victoria.

"Yo' got the paper?" he asked. "Dan kin write his name—jes' like I done with Queen Victoria."

Kennedy produced a form of agreement, which he wrote on a blank paper, and Dan laboriously affixed his signature: D WilLiAMS. Kennedy studied the strange lettering, and decided it would do if there was any future question. He had his men open several cases, and placed the articles on the ground. Dan took these things down to his canoe, but when he returned, he found his other belongings had been taken out of the house and thrown on the ground.

He stared at Kennedy, who was busy directing his men. Dan was angry at the rude way in which his property had been tossed out on the ground, but he decided to say nothing. He did not quite know what to say to a white man in a case of this sort.

He picked up his belongings and carried them down to his canoe. He wondered whether Thela had seen his property on the ground. If so, she would wonder why he had permitted such an indignity. He knew he should have expressed himself; he should have told Kennedy that he had no right to treat the property of Daniel Williams with such disrespect. This would have assured all who heard that he was not a handyman or cook, to be treated like a slave.

But somehow when the situation arose, Dan had not been able to speak out; now he had to suffer the shame of knowing this.

Dan set about the task of building a new house. There were pieces of wood, and an old stove which he took from one of the abandoned miners' shacks. There was enough stovepipe to make a chimney; and soon he had built the walls of a shack and laid beams across the top which he covered with boards. There was no door, but he managed to find a piece of cloth to cover the door opening.

Only Banjo Mike had regarded the settlement with Kennedy as unsatisfactory; and one day he explained this to Dan. Kennedy had been able to buy him off very cheaply, he said; but why had the factor been willing to pay anything? If Dan had no right to the house, why did not Kennedy have him thrown off the place, and be done with it? He must have known the place belonged to Dan.

Dan thought this over; then one day he went over to the factor's store, and asked him for more payment for the house.

Kennedy looked at the big Negro, and remembered all he had heard. This man was known as a troublemaker, as many of the Hudson's Bay Company's traders had reported. He must not be placed in a position where Dan could cause trouble.

He told Dan that it was too late to talk about more payments; he had signed the paper, and that was the end of it.

Dan shuffled his big feet, and stared at the ground.

Finally he said Banjo Mike had talked to him; and this aroused Kennedy's anger.

"Tell him to come and talk to me," he said, in a loud voice.

Dan returned to his shack, but he said nothing to Banjo Mike about the rebuff he had received. There was a change in Kennedy's attitude; Dan did not understand exactly why, but he knew that Kennedy did not regard him as a man to trade with on even terms.

One day Dan shot a deer that had wandered close to the beach. He shot at the deer from the front of his shack, and the deer dropped. Kennedy saw the shot, and he walked over.

"How about selling me the deer?" he said. "I need meat—the stuff I've got is old and dried out."

"Yo' want some of the meat?" Dan asked.

"No," Kennedy said, impatiently. "I don't want a damned thing from you—I just want to buy the meat. Sell it—do you understand?"

Dan shook his head. He had never "sold" meat. When he killed a deer or moose, there was always enough for everyone. But he looked curiously at Kennedy.

"Yo' gonna give me somethin' for the deer?" he asked finally.

"Yes—how much do you want?"

"Twelve ca'tridges," Dan said. Kennedy went back to his store, and in a few minutes returned with twelve bullets for Dan's gun.

"Why did you ask for twelve?" he asked, curiously.

"There was twelve apossles," Dan said, looking at the factor. "Yo' don' know about the twelve apossles?"

Kennedy had heard many tales of the Negro's strange talk about the Bible, and it had even been reported that he had baptized some of the Indians. He nodded with some haste, and assured Dan he knew of the twelve apostles.

Within a remarkably short time, Dan had his house built, filling the cracks with moss which Thela gathered from the woods and puttying this with clay. At night Dan burned wood in the stove, since the air was still cold outside; and he often read parts of his torn Bible to the Indian girl, and now and then sang hymns. Many of these he had learned down in Georgia, but he no longer adhered strictly to the text of the hymns.

One day when Kennedy came to offer twelve bullets for a deer, Dan shook his head. He had stored up a good deal of ammunition, furnishing meat for the factor. Now he wanted twelve plugs of tobacco. This was a lot of tobacco, and Kennedy shook his head.

"I'll give you two plugs," he said.

It was Dan's turn to shake his head. Then, he suggested that if Kennedy would give him twelve plugs, he would consider this payment for several deer. The factor shook his head once more. He knew the stubborn character of the Negro; and he felt that this was the time to take a firm position—to let the black man know who was the boss.

"You work for me—and let your wife sew for me?" he asked. "Twelve plugs of tobacco would be fair for one week's work."

Dan stared at the man for a few seconds, trying to adjust his mind to the rather complex nature of this sort of bargain. Finally he shook his head.

"Dan don' work for no one," he said. "An' Dan's woman don'

work—you hear that? You better shoot some of your own deer!"

"All right," Kennedy said. "You keep the meat and I'll keep the tobacco."

He turned away and walked back to the trading post, leaving Dan in a state of growing perplexity. He felt that somehow Kennedy had gotten the better of him, but he did not know in what way. He saw the young man walking toward his house, and anger suddenly came into Dan's mind. It pushed forward, crowding out other thoughts. He growled some words aloud, without knowing what he was saying. He had sufficient meat to feed the whole camp, and he had little tobacco; yet the factor, who had no meat and a lot of tobacco, had refused to trade with him.

He looked across the space between his shack and the factor's house, which was about two hundred yards away, and muttered aloud:

"Yo' ain't got no damn right to my house—tha's Dan's house, by contrac' with Queen Victoria."

This satisfied him for a while, but the satisfaction did not last. A queer cloud had come over the horizon of Dan's life. He was no longer master of anything. Even his ability to shoot a deer meant nothing, since the trader had walked away without trading his tobacco for the deer meat!

Dan slept poorly, thinking about the foolish way in which he had allowed himself to be tricked by the young factor. However, in about a week Kennedy came over to his house again. He was low in his supply of meat, although Dan did not know this; and he felt it would be wise to re-establish a basis for trading with the big Negro, who could shoot deer with such uncanny skill.

Dan was elated at Kennedy's change of attitude. He wanted to do something to show that he felt no anger against the factor. He knew Kennedy needed someone to sew for him, so he promptly offered the services of Thela to mend a few things for the factor.

"We got plenty of meat," he said. "Yo' go ahead an' take some!"

Kennedy looked at the Negro with a puzzled frown. A few days ago he had not been able to get the deer meat for two plugs of tobacco; now he was getting it for nothing!

He decided he had underestimated Dan's stupidity. He was even more simple than he had supposed! When Dan asked the factor if he would remain and have some food, Kennedy agreed. He was not particularly anxious to eat the kind of food he supposed was cooked in the pieced-together shack, but he felt he must study this Negro better in order to gauge the extent of his simplicity.

The food was surprisingly good, and Kennedy ate heartily. He seldom had cooked food at the trading post except when Dan provided fresh meat. He did not raise the question of meat again; but when he left, Dan gave him a large piece and refused even a single plug of tobacco in exchange.

Banjo Mike had departed from the fort, heading into the mountains to cover his spring trading circuit, so Dan had no one with whom he could discuss this thing. He talked to Thela, however, explaining to her that the factor understood his importance now, and his relations with Queen Victoria, and Mr. Kennedy would unquestionably be a good neighbor.

Thela sat up throughout the night, sewing a pair of moccasins for the factor, which Dan had asked her to make; and the following day he sent her over with them. When she returned, she had a small bag filled with tobacco. It was not the ordinary Cavendish tobacco, but a fine, grained tobacco, which Dan smoked with much enjoyment. She also had a little bag of mustard seed.

Dan was delighted at this display of friendliness by the factor. He would gladly have furnished meat for the entire settlement, asking only a few bullets to shoot the deer with; but Kennedy made no further proposals about meat.

The new factor was a shrewd young man. He watched carefully to note Dan's reaction to each new event; in this way he developed a store of information which would enable him to meet successfully any new situation which Dan might create. There was a possibility that he might get Dan to work for him—an objective which he had in mind from the beginning. But it would have to be on strict terms, set by the trader. Dan must know who was the boss.

Dan watched his store of bullets diminish; and he did not know how to replenish the supply unless Kennedy should offer bullets again for deer meat. This was a situation which Kennedy also understood; he knew almost to a bullet how much ammunition Dan possessed. He decided that the next time Dan approached him to trade for bullets, the question of work would be brought up.

However, an unexpected event changed the factor's plan materially. This was the arrival of the Beaver Indians at Fort St. John.

Indians know when a new factor has arrived at a post, and they lose little time reaching him. In this case, Banjo Mike had undoubtedly apprised the Beavers in various villages of the arrival of the young factor, Mr. Kennedy. And before anyone knew what happened, the bush was alive with Indians.

They came with their squaws and children, apparently for a protracted visit. The women arrived, carrying burdens, brawling and shouting at each other and at their children. The braves stalked in after the women, in a quiet and dignified manner. Tents were put up in helter-skelter fashion, with no order in their location. The women hurried down to the river for water, and the braves stood around, silently surveying the new settlement.

Kennedy knew they had come to trade. What he did not know was that the first trading with a new factor is always a test. Fox skins are brought with patches, cleverly covered with other pieces of fur; and fox noses are sewed on rabbit skins. Beaver skins are traded by weight; often an industrious Indian will strip off some membrane and fill the interior with sand, which weighs more than ordinary pelts but is seldom noticed until the skins arrive back at the Company storage places, where there is a more careful scrutiny.

These tricks are not designed to cheat anyone. They merely expose the extent of skill and knowledge which the new factor possesses, and he will be dealt with accordingly. Old-timers watch for such devices, and trading is quickly established on an equitable basis. But newcomers must learn how to trade.

Many of these skins, filled with sand or patched up, had been in the Beaver villages for years, since they dared not offer them to Banjo Mike or any of the experienced Company traders. However, there was always the chance of learning something about a new trader.

Komaxala arrived among the first groups, and moved into Dan's area, where his tent was established. Bedodid was with him, and she went immediately to Thela.

The following day Dan went over to the trading post. Kennedy regarded him sourly. He had observed the Indians who had come to Dan's shack; and he knew the stories about Dan's having lived with the Indians. Dan told the factor that the Indians had arrived to trade.

"Yes—I see," Kennedy said shortly. "They did not come to the post. Do you know why?"

"These Indians don' know you, Massa Kennedy," Dan said. "Maybe yo' all needs some help in tradin' with 'em."

"It is not the policy of the Company to deal in that kind of trading," Kennedy said, his voice and manner quite abrupt. He had no idea how Dan figured in the trading; but he knew of the unsavory reputation of the giant Negro, and he was determined that Dan would not become a party to any of the Company's business transactions. A handyman at the trading post—yes; not a partner in business. Heaven forbid!

Dan hesitated; and then he left. He knew some of the tricks of the Indians, since he had lived with them. He even recognized some of the old pelts. And Thela knew how they traded. Dan might have told the young factor how to trade with the Beavers. But Kennedy's manner annoyed him; and he left the trading post with anger against the factor again in his heart.

CHAPTER NINETEEN

Komaxala was the first to approach Kennedy. He walked into the factor's store with a bundle of skins, and threw them on the floor. Then he found a space among some boxes, and sat down. He seemed to be sleeping, but his half-closed eyes were watching every movement Kennedy made.

The young man stooped to pick up some of the pelts. He examined them, rubbing the furs together. Then he put his hand inside the skins to feel whether there were any rents.

Komaxala watched this show of expert craftsmanship, knowing it concealed the factor's ignorance of trading. A smart trader would have glanced at the skins, without appearing to notice them. If there were things a keen eye could detect, he would detect them. Komaxala knew there was a loose foot on one of the skins—a foot born in the kennel of a white dog, which had been sewed to the fox pelt. The factor did not observe this. And he had failed to shake the beaver skins before weighing them, to sift out any sand in the lining of membrane.

Kennedy was nervous, and he took longer than was customary to appraise the skins. He was aware that he was under observation; he had been forewarned of many such things. It was a different matter, however, to be told what to expect, and to detect it. He was prepared to refuse any defective pelts with great scorn; yet he could find no defects upon which to base a refusal. Finally he turned toward Komaxala, but the old chief had rolled over on his side and appeared to be sleeping.

Kennedy spoke to him sharply; when Komaxala finally rolled back slowly and seemed to awaken, he gaped at the factor as if he did not understand the reason for the interruption.

Then, with a wave of his hand—as if he suddenly realized that the factor was talking about buying skins—he indicated he was no longer interested in the matter.

"Bad skins sell cheap," he said. "These good skins—no sell." He rolled over again, presumably overpowered by the desire for sleep.

Kennedy recognized these signs. Komaxala wished to show little interest in selling the skins; yet he had brought them to the post, and therefore he must have wished to sell them. The factor waved his hand in a gesture of contempt.

"They are not good skins," he said. "If you have taken much trouble to bring these skins to me, you have wasted your time. I cannot pay much for them."

Komaxala leaped suddenly to his feet.

"You have spoken of my skins—the skins of Komaxala, the chief of a great tribe! A young man speaks hastily; a brave man speaks seldom. An old man speaks only when wisdom prompts him. Komaxala has only this to say: I will leave your house, where I sought rest, so that there will not be enmity between you and my people."

Komaxala spoke in Beaver, which Kennedy understood. The chief then stooped over and snatched the skins from the floor. Holding them under his arm, he stalked toward the door, slowly and with dignity. When he reached the door, he turned again.

"The trader they call Banjo Mike has looked at my skins," he said, his sharp black eyes looking directly at the factor. "They are better skins than he can afford to buy, and he has taken lesser skins . . . These I will take to Dunvegan, and see if the chief of your company at that place knows the value of trading for skins."

He spoke slowly, in the Beaver tongue; Kennedy stared at him with desperation in his eyes. He faced a bitter alternative: either calling back this chief, whose skins he had all but rejected, and begging him to trade—which might end his standing as a trader with these Indians; or allowing the Indians to go to Kennedy's superior at Dunvegan, in which case, if the skins were valuable, Kennedy would be sure to receive a Company reprimand.

Komaxala understood exactly what was passing through Kennedy's mind; and with a sign that all dealings were ended, he turned and left the trading post.

Kennedy saw him walk directly to the shack where Dan lived, and the sight enraged him. Dan had offered to act as intermediary with the Indians, and Kennedy had refused. Now the factor might be forced to the galling necessity of going to Dan and asking him to intercede.

A good deal of Kennedy's feeling of superiority had evaporated; and he resolved that nothing would stand between his reopening trading with Komaxala. He watched all day as members of the Indian party gathered at the tent of the chief, which was only a few steps from the shack of the black man.

In the evening Dan came over to the factor's trading post; and Kennedy, his mouth puckered in a worried expression, waited for the Negro. Dan approached the door of the trading post, but he did not enter.

"We is goin' to Dunvegan to he'p the Injuns," he said, jerking a thumb toward the shack where he lived. Thela stood at the door watching them. "I is gonna be the feller to do the talkin'."

"You mean you are helping the redskins to trade?" Kennedy asked. Then, after an instant of hesitation, he said, "Look here, Dan—you live here. You need things from the store. You talk for me—I speak Beaver, but maybe it is better for you to talk. Tell the chief I am here to buy skins. I have to buy them as cheap as possible, but you tell him I'll be fair."

It was humiliating for George Kennedy to ask Dan to intercede, but he saw no other way. He watched Dan's face closely, thinking that he could read in the Negro's face what was going on in his mind.

Finally it was agreed that Dan would speak to Komaxala again. He felt a renewed sense of importance; he was now a man through whom the trading would take place. Komaxala listened to Dan; then he suggested there should be a council around a fire. Perhaps the trader would bring tobacco as a gift, a concession to the good will of both parties. The meeting was arranged, and Kennedy arrived at the fire, bringing tobacco. By this time Komaxala understood thoroughly the kind of a man with whom he was dealing—a young man, ambitious to get ahead in the trading business, yet a man who would need some time to learn how to trade. Such a man could be fooled easily.

They agreed to bargain again, and went over to the trading store. The pelts were laid out, after an exchange of amenities in which Kennedy assured the chief he wished to trade for skins. Komaxala's face remained rigid and calm, never betraying his thoughts. His black eyes darted swiftly about, studying each movement of the factor, listening to each word, weighing the intangible factors of trading.

Kennedy, on the other hand, was so nervous he made no attempt to study the chief. He spoke rapidly, sometimes in English and sometimes in Beaver. When he showed the articles he wished to offer in trade, Komaxala barely glanced at them, and often tossed them back on the pile of goods without so much as a fleeting examination. He knew, of course, what the articles were like; they were standard trading, and he knew to a fraction their worth in skin values.

Komaxala finally arranged a system of wooden sticks, which he used to count the articles the factor put forth. After a certain number of sticks had been piled up, a pelt would be tossed out. This was a good way of counting, except that Komaxala now and then took sticks back from his pile, claiming an article was not what he wanted. Kennedy, in his effort to keep track of his own goods and the pelts—and also Komaxala's sticks—lost track of everything.

Komaxala was skilled at trading. He had sold skins to many kinds of people, and he knew that talking often distracts the mind of the other trader from the business at hand. So he continued to throw in questions and comments, which Dan interpreted.

Bedodid also was permitted at the parley, since she was the

wife of the chief. She handled the skins frequently, and now and then examined a skin which had already been accepted by the factor. Some of these found their way back under her ample garment, and when the trading was finished, she brought out three skins which she explained she had reserved for buying needles and things for herself.

By this time Kennedy was so baffled at the exchange of skins and sticks for his goods that he gave her twice the value of the skins in articles from his store, meanwhile watching Komaxala and the other Indians at the council to be sure they did not outwit him.

As soon as Komaxala departed, more Indians entered. Kennedy continued to barter with these Indians, whose sole object was to give their chief time to collect his belongings and depart. It was only after considerable trading, during which additional pelts were offered and then taken back, that Kennedy's helper—a half-breed who went by the name of Nick—nudged his employer and pointed to certain defects in the skins.

"Whose are these?" Kennedy demanded, holding up the skins. One pelt which Dan recognized—having seen it four years before at the Beaver village—was a combination of fox and rabbit, and would have passed unnoticed except that the thread had parted, leaving the patch open at one side. Kennedy turned to Dan.

"You are responsible for this. I should never have let a damned nigger get into this thing!" He was trembling with fury, and his reddish hair was damp with perspiration. Suddenly he ran to the door, and saw Komaxala's party preparing to shove off in their canoes.

"Get them back here!" he roared at Dan. "Komaxala! Come back—I say, come back!"

Dan stood beside the factor, but said nothing. He was not certain what had happened—and when Kennedy called him a "damned nigger," he was both angry and alarmed. This was the kind of talk that often came before a beating, and he glanced toward his shack, intending to make a run for it and get his gun if necessary.

The half-breed, Nick, picked up several skins. All were torn and defective. Kennedy had run halfway to the beach, shouting for Komaxala to come back; but the Indian canoes pushed out into the river, and finally the factor came back. His face was flushed, and his eyes betrayed panic. He had given up most of the Company's stores for a pile of worthless skins. Dan stood beside the doorway, his arms hanging slackly at his sides; and Nick stood in the door, holding the torn pelts.

Kennedy stopped and stared at Dan. The heavy lips of the black man were parted in a smile. It was an apologetic smile, and Dan would have liked to explain how sorry he was that the factor had been outmaneuvered in the trading. But Kennedy was in no mood for fine variances of feeling.

"You damned black ape!" he shouted at Dan. "You dirty nigger! Get the hell out of my place—and don't ever come back! I'll report you to Dunvegan—I'll drive you out of this place——"

Dan walked back to his shack. Being called a "dirty nigger" did not bother him particularly. He had often been called that and worse. But he saw no reason for Kennedy's anger at him. He wished he had spoken back to the factor; the shame of being sworn at, particularly in front of the half-breed, Nick, was unendurable. It diminished his position and was worse than the curses themselves.

The next day Kennedy went over to Dan's shack. He had recovered some of his former calm, and he told Dan quite coldly that he had "reported the matter" to his superiors; unless Dan left Fort St. John, a constable would be dispatched to arrest him.

Dan looked at the factor in astonishment.

"What in hell yo' astin' me to leave for?" he said suddenly. "This is my land, Mister Kennedy—yo' got no right to ast me to leave!"

Kennedy's thin Scottish face showed no humor. His eyes glinted.

"Either get out—or go to jail," he said.

"What do I got to go to jail for?" Dan asked. "I ain't done nothin'—'cept to act like yo' ast me, talkin' with the Injuns!"

236

"You will be charged with inciting the Indians to riot—with disturbing the peace of this country. The Company does not tolerate that kind of thing—as you well know!"

"What in the hell the Company got to do with me?" Dan asked. "I ain't workin' for the Company no mo', Massa Kennedy! I gotta contrac'——"

Kennedy's teeth fairly gritted.

"Don't give me that story about Queen Victoria again!" he said, his voice rising. "If I hadn't listened to that damned nonsense—and Banjo Mike—I'd have run you off long ago! Now get out! I won't be responsible——"

He turned and strode back to his store. That night he sent a dispatch to Dunvegan, requesting that papers of prosecution be drawn up against one Daniel Williams for molesting the properly authorized agents of the Hudson's Bay Company, acting in the service of Her Majesty the Queen.

Roderick MacFarlane, the district manager for the Hudson's Bay Company, had come down from Vermilion to Dunvegan. He saw Kennedy's dispatch, and he studied it carefully. George Kennedy was a relative of his wife, and he owed the young man more than average consideration. But he wondered if the assignment to open the new post at Fort St. John had not been too much for an untried factor. The reputation of this Negro outlaw, known as Nigger Dan, was notorious; perhaps it would take a more seasoned man to bring him to heel. It might be well to look into the matter personally.

Meanwhile, Dan himself had composed a note. He sat in his shack throughout the night, brooding upon the matter. He had done nothing that was wrong—God would know that he had acted in His interests. Yet the Company was asking him to leave—driving him off his land!

Once during the night he stepped out and called out to Kennedy.

"Yo' is a heathen, Massa Kennedy!" he roared. "Yo' ain't even read the Bible! Yo' don' even know they's twelve apossles——"

With this parting shot, he went back into the shack. He took a piece of wrapping paper and the stub of a pencil and wrote out with much effort this note:

KENedy I hear by Worne you that CoM an GETT yor pERsNoL PRoPPiTy if ENy YOU HavE GoTT oF My PREMEEis IN 24 HoURs THEN KEEP AWAy BEcos I sHALL NoT BE TRuBBLED Nor TRod On oNLy By HER Most NoBEL MAJEsTy GoVERMENT.

D WiLLiAMS.

Kennedy found the note tacked to his door in the morning. He tore it from the door; and that day he sent another dispatch to MacFarlane at Dunvegan.

MacFarlane was now quite concerned. He studied the two reports carefully. Then he sent word to the "Justice of the Peace," a Mr. Butler, whose judicial domain extended over the territories of "Rupert's Land and the North-West." He advised him that one Daniel Williams, a notorious outlaw, was in the area of Fort St. John, and might be "making trouble." The charge of "making trouble" was familiar to Justice Butler. It consisted of everything, from ordinary hell-raising to murder, that might annoy the Hudson's Bay Company. So Justice Butler decided it was time to issue a "judicial memorandum," and he did so. It said:

Various circumstances having occurred in the neighbourhood of the Hudson's Bay Company Fort, known as St. John's, on the Peace River, of a nature to lead to the assumption that a breach of the peace is liable to arise out of the question of disputed ownership, in a plot of land on the North shore of the River, on which the Hudson's Bay Company have erected buildings to serve as their future place of business, and on which it is asserted one Daniel Williams a person of colour, formerly lived, this is to notify all persons concerned in this question, that no belief of ownership, no former or present possession, will be held in any way to excuse or palliate the slightest infringement of law, or to sanction any act of violence being

238

committed, or to occasion any threats being made use of by any of said parties which might lead to a breach of the peace.

Executed by me, as Justice of the Peace, for Rupert's Land and the North-West, this 22nd day of April, 1873. W. F. Butler.

There is no record that this formidable document ever reached Dan Williams, or if it did, that he read it. And there is, of course, even less reason to believe that he would have understood it, if he had read it.

MacFarlane was not a man to rely on notices and judicial memoranda to do his business, however. He was an old hand at Indian trading; and since George Kennedy was his protégé, he knew his weakness as well as his strength. In this case, he wanted no weakness. So he called in Mr. W. C. King.

The Beaver Indians and their chief, Komaxala, were well known to King. "A damned supercilious lot" he called them. He had no doubt he could cope with them; and he expressed even less doubt that he could cope with the Negro "outlaw," Nigger Dan.

Within a few weeks, King arrived at Fort St. John and Kennedy departed. Kennedy expressed disappointment in bitter terms.

"That damned nigger is responsible!" he told his successor. He pointed toward Dan's shack, where smoke was curling up through the blue morning air. King nodded.

"He's had a notorious reputation," he said. "The Government ought to have run him off long ago . . . Killed a French trader, I hear—up in the Beaver country a few years back. And I hear he done in some miners, right here, five or six years back. A damned outlaw—a disgrace—nuisance to the Company."

King spoke in close, clipped sentences. His thoughts were so well formulated on all matters that he found no need for extended discussions of anything. He was a man of prompt and vigorous opinion.

For some days those who lived at the settlement—including a scattering of Indians who had drifted in and set up their huts, hoping to find work from time to time, and enjoying the economic security of living near a post, where there was always food—saw little of the new factor. He worked inside the post and did not speak to anyone.

Dan was highly pleased with the arrival of King. It was a vindication of his importance, and his relations with Queen Victoria, that Kennedy had to leave the trading post. As soon as he got around to it, which might be any day, he intended to step over to the trading post and speak to the new factor. He would show that he was a good neighbor, a good man to have around, particularly when it came to dealing with the Indians.

A week later King's wife arrived. She was a pleasant, smiling lady, of middle age, and well adjusted to the life of the remote frontiers of the Hudson's Bay Company domain.

Shortly after this a half-breed named La Flume came to Dan's shack. He was well known in the country: more white than Indian—the descendant of French adventurers who had penetrated the Saskatchewan country even before the missionaries. He had traveled from one side of Canada to the other on foot, on horseback, and in canoes. He spoke most of the Indian dialects, and had been with the Kings for many years.

Dan recognized La Flume from earlier days, when he came to the door of his shack in response to the half-breed's call.

"You got a woman with you?" La Flume asked. Dan nodded; and he began to explain the circumstances in which he had made a living woman out of a dead one, with the help of God and the proper use of the Bible.

La Flume made a quick gesture.

"Mister King say you 'Get out!' he said, and returned to the trading post.

Dan was puzzled at this unexpected contact with the new factor. He thought perhaps he should have gone over earlier to speak to him, and suiting action to the thought, he strode across the area between his house and the trading store.

King was standing in the doorway. He held a rifle in one hand, and his sharp eyes were fixed upon Dan as he shambled up to the doorstep.

"I's jes' wantin' to say 'Hello,' Massa King," Dan said. "I jes' came over to see what I could do maybe."

King was a wiry man with a square jaw and a bristling manner. He stood for several seconds, looking Dan over from head to foot. Finally he said:

"You get out of here—that's what you can do! You and that damned whore living with you—get out, that's all I've got to say!"

Dan stared at the new factor, and then he doubled his fists.

"Yo' ain't gonna get no trouble, 'lessen you asts for it!" he said, finally. "If yo' asts for it, yo' gonna get it! This here is my land yo're on—but yo' can stay here, like I said Massa Kennedy can stay. But don' yo' go callin' my woman a whore——"

King snapped his fingers.

"Get out!" he said, angrily. "Keep away from this place!"

He turned suddenly and disappeared into the house. Dan glanced around to see if La Flume had overheard the talk, but the half-breed was nowhere to be seen. Dan turned slowly and shuffled back to his shack.

He sat for some time in front of his shack, staring at the ground. Thela was inside, mending his clothes, but he had no desire to speak with her now. He had told her before he went to the trading post to speak to the new factor that everything now was settled . . . There would now be friendship between himself and the people from the Company. But there was not much friendliness in the new factor's manner.

Finally Dan bowed his head, and held his clasped hands in front of his face.

The next day Dan awakened to the sound of axes ringing in the morning air. They were close to his shack, and he jumped out of his bunk and went out of the door. Some of King's men were cutting down trees—and they were on Dan's land.

He walked over to the men.

"They's plenty of trees," he said. "Why yo' all cuttin' on my land?"

In a few minutes King came across the clearing. Dan waited for him to say something, but when the factor remained silent, he blurted out the same inquiry.

King asked him how he knew it was his land. Dan pointed to the sticks which he had staked out.

"All them sticks is marks," he said. "I got my name on 'em."

"Did you register the claim?" King asked; and then more sharply: "Look here, I'm tired of all this sort of thing about the Queen that I hear you've been saying! Kennedy treated you like a child, when he should have shot at you for trespassing. Unless you have registered this land with Mr. Butler, the Justice of the Peace—you have no right to any of it! Not even the land your damned shack stands on! Do you understand that—you damned black outlaw!"

He spoke furiously; and without waiting for Dan to reply, he turned on his heel, gesturing to the workmen to continue their cutting operations.

Dan walked back to his shack. His face was clouded, and he tried to remember what Banjo Mike had told him. Nobody said anything about having to "register" the land. The magic word "register" had knocked the props out from under him. He looked at his shack as he walked toward it, and shook his huge head. It wasn't a good house—not like the trading post the Company had built for Mr. Kennedy. But it had been his home —and now maybe it belonged to the Company.

For many hours Dan sat brooding. Thela did not know the trouble, but she knew the expressions on the face of the man she had lived with for four years. Her black eyes became warm with silent suffering as she watched Dan. All afternoon he said nothing.

But in the evening, while he munched the food she had prepared, he suddenly raised his head and looked at her.

"I gonna get some wood," he said, in a low voice. "Tha's God's wood they cuttin'—even if it ain't mine! I gonna get some."

And so that night he stood outside the house and sang hymns in a voice that rang across the river; King came several times to the door to stare at the black man, framed in the light of his own doorway. He muttered a few words, but said nothing to Dan; and finally his house was dark.

After Dan had sung all the hymns he could remember, he walked out to the pile of cordwood the factor's helpers had cut during the day. It was the beginning of winter, and light snow was on the ground. This showed his heavy tracks as he tramped to and from the factor's woodpile.

The next morning King rose early, and when he came out he saw the tracks of the Negro, clearly outlined in the snow.

CHAPTER TWENTY

King was a man with ideas. He was not a young man, but he had the force of a man of much younger years. He also had principles; and when anyone violated his principles, he knew how to strike back!

It was one of his principles that what belonged to anyone working for the Company belonged to the Company itself. Therefore the wood Dan had stolen was property stolen from the Hudson's Bay Company.

That day he had some of the cordwood brought from the pile where the workmen had stacked it into his living quarters at the trading post. He took a handful of cartridges, and carefully pried open the shells. The gunpowder was collected and tapped lightly into small holes in the cordwood.

The next morning Dan was singing in front of his shack. The stove was burning inside, sending up curls of light smoke into the crisp morning air. The ground was white with snow

243

that had fallen during the night, and there were not even tracks to and from the woodpile.

Suddenly there was a report, like the sound of a tree breaking. Dan looked up and saw the top of the chimney jump into the air and fall back. Part of the roof seemed to have bulged, and black smoke was coming out of the shack.

He rushed into the room and dragged Thela out. It looked as if the Devil himself had given a kick at the stove. It was half on one side, and fire was pouring from the grate door. Dan went back and beat out the fire, but the sides of his house had been split and the stove was damaged almost beyond repair.

After the fire had cooled down, Dan went back into the shack and tried to put the stove together. It was not too badly damaged, and he managed to fix the grate door so it would shut. The stovepipe could be fastened together with wire; and while it leaked smoke into the room, it was not as bad as staying outside in the cold.

The next day King came by the shack, and stood for some time looking at it. Dan stared at him, but said nothing. He was not sure how the factor had arranged to have the Devil kick over his stove, but he was sure he had had a hand in it.

For a couple of days nothing happened. Dan had stolen enough wood from the factor's pile to last several days, so he made no more nocturnal visits for fuel supplies. And then it happened again!

This time the explosion blew the stove apart, and some of the burning wood struck Thela. Her face and body were burned, and Dan quickly pulled her outside.

This time Dan decided to move his belongings out of the shack. While Thela was applying to the burned parts of her face and body some grease from a mixture of herbs and *klina* she kept in a leather bag, Dan set up a fireplace outside. This was work he never permitted Thela to do; and although it was not according to her notion of the division of labor between a man and his mate, she always followed his desires.

Now she sat before the fire, watching him. In the years since

244

she had left the Beaver village, her body had not grown old; but her face was lined with strange seams, caused by the drawing of the muscles on one side of her face. Dan observed this, and it seemed that she was growing older. Only the fire in her eyes and the strength of her body remained; her face was that of an old woman.

Dan wondered if perhaps his wife, whom he had left back in Georgia, were also praying to God—perhaps asking him to punish Dan for his sins. He shook his head, and gazed broodingly at the fire. Was God punishing him for living with Thela? The factor had called her a "whore," and Dan knew this was a terrible word for a woman . . . Yet Thela was a good woman, and the daughter of a chief. She needed Dan's help because she could not speak, and it did not seem to Dan that God would punish him for helping her.

The night air was cold, and yet he did not want to go back into the house while the Devil was kicking over things. So he gathered his leather sleeping bags and covered Thela and himself, and they slept under the stars, while the fire burned down.

In the house of the factor there was some discussion that night between King and his wife. She heard the dogs barking and asked him the cause of it. The dogs were prize animals, and the factor was quite proud of them; it was quite natural that Mrs. King would feel concerned about them.

The factor laughed; then he told her how he had put gunpowder in the cordwood that Dan had stolen. Mrs. King looked at her husband carefully, and then said:

"You must go over and see what happened. They may be hurt!"

The factor finally pulled on his heavy coat and made his way through the snow toward Dan's shack. He could see them running out in the snow, dragging things from the house. Dan's roaring and shouting could be heard above everything, and King was sure no one who was hurt could yell that much.

He returned and reassured his wife.

The dogs did not go to sleep, however. The strange happenings at the house across the clearing were clearly a matter of interest to them, and they began to sniff around the pile of things Dan had dragged out of his shack to move them from the fire. There was some meat, and this naturally interested the dogs.

Dan heard the noise, and thought wolverines had come prowling around his dismantled home. He rose and snatched a piece of wood from the dying fire.

"Get outa here, yo' damn' devils!" he roared, and thrust the half-burning sticks at the animals. The dogs snapped back, and Dan hurled the sticks at them. One of the dogs leaped at him; he caught the animal in mid-air and with a powerful heave threw the dog bodily into the fire.

The animal jumped out and ran screaming into the night.

King had jumped from his bed at the sudden infuriated barking of the dogs, and ran to the door. He was in time to see the powerful body of the Negro, naked against the glow of the fire, swinging his dog in an arc through the air. King's stomach turned sick as he saw the animal flung into the fire, and then watched it dash from the burning pyre.

"The damned nigger has killed my dog!" he screamed to his wife; and brandishing his fist in the direction of Dan's shack, he roared into the emptiness of the night, "I'll kill ye, ye murderin' black devil! I'll kill ye!"

The next morning the half-breed, La Flume, was at Dan's shack at daybreak. King's dogs had been virtually destroyed, he said. They had come home during the night, their coats badly burned and one of them with a broken leg.

"What yo' talk to me for?" Dan asked angrily. "Some damned wolves come in the night, an' I drove 'em off. Ain't I got a right to do that?"

La Flume shook his head.

"Mr. King is plenty damned mad," he said. Shortly afterward King came over. His sharp eyes were smoldering with wrath, and he lost no time coming to the point.

"You killed one of my dogs last night," he said. "That dog was my property, and you'll either pay for it or get out! You stole my wood, and now you've killed my dogs!"

246

Dan looked at the factor, and suddenly he realized that King was an enemy. King had tried to kill Thela and himself, and now perhaps he had sent the dogs to destroy his food. He stood more than a foot above King, and his powerful body made the factor look like a dwarf. Now there was anger in his black eyes, and his body filled with the pressure of his breathing, the way a hurricane fills the air dangerously before it blows into a violent storm.

King paid no attention to these signs. He shook a trembling finger at Dan.

"You've had my last warning!" he said. "You and that damned trollop you're livin' with clear out—or I'll clear ye out! Do you understand that?"

Dan's eyes glowed; but he merely said:

"Yo' ain't drivin' me nowhere, Mister King. I gotta right to live here—by Queen Victoria——"

"Damn you and your stupidity!" King shouted. "I'll have you jailed for that!"

"Yo're dogs et my food las' night," Dan went on stubbornly. "Yo' gotta get me some more food. We ain't got nothin' lef' to eat."

King left, swearing savagely as he walked back to his store. During the day Dan thought about the matter of food. Some of his supplies were left, but many of them had been ruined by the dogs.

He knew where stores of pemmican and dried meat were kept in the trading store; and that night he walked quietly up to the side of the house where the storeroom wall was located and cut away part of the calking. The hole was not large, but he was able to reach in and take several pieces of pemmican.

The following day King observed the break in his walls, but he said nothing. He did not even repair the holes. Instead he arranged several pieces of pemmican near the aperture, after cutting them open and pouring in a weak mixture of strychnine and resin oil, which would prevent freezing.

By this time the feud between the factor and the man they called Nigger Dan was no secret to anyone in the settlement.

The half-breeds working at the trading post, who had been brought upriver from Fort Vermilion and from Dunvegan, knew that someone had broken into King's storeroom; and they knew he had laid poisoned pemmican as a trap.

La Flume even walked over to the Negro's half-ruined house and advised him to leave.

"Mr. King is bad feller when he's mad," he told Dan. "He plenty damned mad now! Much better you go away."

Dan shook his head. He was sure that God would be on his side, now that He knew what the factor was doing against him . . . But of course no one told Dan about the poisoned pemmican.

That night Dan sneaked over to the store again, and found the crack in the wall he had made the night before. He took quite a load of the dried meat, which happily was within reach of his long arm, and then plastered the moss back in the crack so the wind would not blow through it and reveal Dan's scheme.

The following day Dan looked across at the trader's house, and saw King standing at the door with his wife. It suddenly struck Dan that he had not demonstrated to King how well he could shoot. Perhaps this would impress the factor. It might make him understand, for one thing, that God was on Dan's side.

Dan took his gun from the corner where he kept it, and went out into the woods. King was standing against the door frame, and Dan decided to shoot a hole through the frame near his head, just to remind the factor that he was dealing with a man who could shoot!

He took aim and fired. King leaped away from the door as if he were stung. Dan laughed in a rolling bellow that could easily be heard at the factor's house. He had seen the slight puff of dust where the bullet struck about two inches above King's head.

King dodged into the house. His wife was pale with fright.

"He'll kill you!" she cried; but King was beside himself with rage.

"That black devil—I'll show him!" he shouted. He went back into his bedroom and took his gun down from the rack. The window faced the open clearing, with Dan's shack clearly in view.

Mrs. King begged him not to shoot.

"There must be something else!" she said. "The man is insane—I know. But he is mild and friendly when he wants to be. The Indian woman is friendly, too—please don't shoot!"

But King was in a rage. The "black devil" had actually tried to kill him. He stood at the window and watched Dan come out of the woods. He walked with his long, shambling stride toward his house. King raised his rifle and fired.

The bullet came so close to Dan that he ducked. Then he turned and ran for his house. Thela had heard the shots, and she ran to the door just as King fired the second time. Dan pushed her quickly back into the house.

"That damn man don' know how to shoot!" he yelled, and made Thela lie on the floor while he peered through a rent in the wall of the shack.

King had accomplished all he wished to. He ejected the shell from the breech-loader, and put it up on the rack. The "black devil" had his lesson. Perhaps this would be the thing needed to drive him away from the place, so there would be peace again at the trading post.

The shooting had shaken Dan's confidence in himself more than anything that had happened. He knew from the reckless way the shots had been fired that the factor intended to hit him. This was a startling realization—that a man like Mr. King would shoot at him.

That night Dan sat brooding again over his troubles; and finally he came to a great decision. He turned to Thela who sat watching him with worried, sorrowful eyes. Dan was munching on the pemmican he had stolen while he explained his decision to her.

"We gotta move away f'om here," he said. "That man ain't tryin' to scare me—he's tryin' to kill me!" He looked at the ragged, fire-blackened walls of his once-fine home, and shook his head. "We gotta pack up an' go," he repeated. "I don' know where we goin', but we gotta go."

He suggested to Thela that she prepare the rest of the pemmican for traveling and gather their other belongings. Early in the morning they would leave, saying nothing to anyone . . . At that moment Dan clasped his hands across his stomach. A violent spasm racked his whole body, and in a matter of seconds he was bent over double, holding his tortured stomach and groaning.

Thela leaped up and ran to his side. She looked at his face, and saw the pain in his eyes. They rolled wildly, and his mouth stiffened. His arms slipped away from his stomach, and he rolled off the chair to the floor.

Thela held his arm, which was limp. She tried to lift his head, but it rolled from side to side; an instant later his body became tense and hard, the corded muscles of his back suddenly drawing his spine backward until it bent like a bow.

She opened her mouth, but she could utter no sound. For several seconds she stared in horror at Dan's twisted face. Then she rose from the floor and ran out into the night.

She knew where La Flume stayed, in a shack behind the trading post. She ran toward this place. La Flume was standing outside the shack when she came up, her eyes wild with fear; and he understood at once what had happened. Dan had eaten the poisoned pemmican. . . .

La Flume did not know any cure for strychnine. It was used to kill wolves, although it was forbidden to use it to kill foxes. He knew also that the black man, Nigger Dan, was a great enemy of the Hudson's Bay Company, and perhaps it was not forbidden to use this poison against enemies of the Company.

Nevertheless, he knew it was not right to let a man die as he had seen wolves die, threshing out their lives in terrible agony. So he ran with the girl back to Dan's shack.

Dan was lying on his back, his coarse lips parted and his teeth bared as he looked upward. His eyes were open. He managed to groan, and then through his teeth he whispered: "Yo' get Massa King—tell him Dan is dyin'——"

250

La Flume went back to the factor's house and told him what happened.

"He's pretty close to die," he said. "He want see you."

King listened, but he shook his head.

"He probably won't die," he said. "But I'll give you something to take to him. It was his own damned fault—the black devil! He was poisoned by the pemmican he stole. . . ."

La Flume took the medicine King gave him, and went back to the shack. Thela was hovering over the Negro, her lips moving in a mute semblance of sound; and she was holding his head off the floor with her hands. The half-breed lifted Dan's head and poured the medicine between his parched lips. Dan was conscious; and he stared at them with terrified eyes.

Immediately after he swallowed the medicine, he vomited. La Flume rolled him over and he retched violently for some time. Thela, as soon as she saw what was happening, ran to the back of the room and took a small bag, from which she sifted powdered herbs. She mixed these with water, and when Dan was able to sit up, she poured the mixture into his mouth.

In a short while Dan was able to sit on the chair. He was weak and helpless, and unable to talk.

"He's fine now," La Flume said, with a sigh. "You better bury the pemmican now—an' then you get the hell out from here right away. Mister King, he's terrible mad."

La Flume carried word of Dan's recovery back to the factor's house. Mrs. King immediately prepared a pot of soup, which she carried down to Dan's shack herself. The giant Negro lay in miserable silence in his bunk, still too weak to speak; and the factor's wife showed Thela how to feed him the soup. Then, before leaving, she said to Dan:

"Do not be angry at my husband for what has happened. You stole the pemmican—that was wrong. My husband does not want to harm anyone, but you have made trouble for us— and for the Company. You helped the Indians cheat Mr. Kennedy, and you have killed many people and robbed trading stores. You cannot expect people to forgive these things."

Dan stared at the woman. He heard what she said, but he

251

was too weak to reply. Finally, as she turned to leave, he managed to mumble, "Dan don' do these things . . . God don' let Dan do these things. . . ."

Mrs. King shook her head. She did not believe him, of course; any criminal will deny his crimes. But she pitied the suffering man, so she went out without saying anything further.

Several days later, when Dan was well enough to sit in front of his shack, wrapped in blankets and staring into the frosty sunlight, the factor came over, walking slowly and deliberately.

He stopped in front of Dan and for some time said nothing. Dan was still too weak to talk much, so he also said nothing.

"I received a message this morning," King said. "The Indians upriver are on their way here. You must get ready to go with them when they leave."

Dan looked up and shook his head.

King nodded firmly. "You will have to go. I have also asked a constable of the Mounted Police to come to this post. If you are not gone when he arrives, he will arrest you—and then you will go to jail."

King turned without a further word, and walked back to his store. After he left, Dan thought a great deal about what he had said. If a constable was on his way to Fort St. John, then Dan would be able to put his complaints before him. He would demand that King be put off his land . . . When Sergeant Bannister of the Canadian Royal Mounted Police arrived, Dan was ready for him. He sent word by La Flume that he wished to see the emissary of the law.

CHAPTER TWENTY-ONE

King was listening to the story of Sergeant Bannister when La Flume arrived.

"It is fortunate that we do not have to go farther," the sergeant was saying. "I had decided to go up through the Beaver country until I got hold of the man . . . But now that he is here, I can take him. The ice is bad now, you know—it may not break up for weeks. We'll have to get him down to Fort Saskatchewan by sled."

King nodded.

"Don't think he'll be easy to take," he warned. "He's dangerous, and he can shoot in a deadly way. He almost killed me, you know . . . Sometimes he is mild, however, and if he feels that way, you may be able to take him without trouble."

The sergeant nodded. "Crazy, eh? Those are the hardest to handle. . . ."

Mrs. King begged the sergeant and his men to be careful, and avoid shooting. Sergeant Bannister smiled at this notion.

"Madam, we always avoid shooting if possible. I will talk to him tomorrow." He turned to La Flume and said, "Tell Williams I'll see him tomorrow."

Dan did not sleep that night. He lay in his bunk, alternately praying and talking aloud. He was worried because Sergeant Bannister had not come to see him. Perhaps he would leave without bothering to see a man who was sick; then Dan would not have the opportunity to lay his complaints before the man who spoke for Queen Victoria.

"Oh, dear Jesus!" he prayed. "Get that Queen Victoria man to come over here! Dan don' wan' to go back with the Indians!"

The next morning Dan began to sing hymns, hoping the "Queen Victoria man" would hear them. He did, and noted it down in his book. "This is important," he told King. "It bears out pretty much what we've heard."

In the middle of the morning Dan started to arise from his bunk, but he was still so weak he slipped and fell. His ankle pained him badly, and he realized that he had sprained it.

The knocking at the door was louder, and through the boards which he had used as a substitute for the leather door flap in winter, he could see that several men were at the door.

"Is Dan Williams in there?" the man shouted.

"Yessir, it's me—Dan Williams! I done busted my leg, I reckon. You'll have to come in."

There was some talk outside, and then a voice said:

"You'll come out or we'll shoot!"

Thela heard the sound of the voices; and now she stood up at the other side of the room. Her eyes were wide with fear, and her tall, straight body seemed to tremble.

"You're under arrest, Daniel Williams," the man at the door said. "The charge is assault with intent to kill. Whatever you say may be used against you . . . Now come out, or we'll shoot!"

Dan stared at the doorway, trying to understand what the words meant.

"I ain't no murderer!" he finally shouted, his voice hoarse with excitement. "I got a complaint——"

Sergeant Bannister had unstrapped his service revolver. He aimed it at the door, and shot. An instant before, Thela had started toward the door, and had opened her mouth and screamed: *Tes-kwa! Tes-kwa! . . . Stop! Stop!*"

These were the first words Thela had uttered since the lightning struck her on the caribou hunt; and they were her last. Sergeant Bannister's bullet struck her in the forehead as she ran across the room, and she fell forward.

Dan's gun lay against the wall. He reached for it at the instant Bannister shot, and almost in the same instant he fired through the door. The bullet struck the policeman in the chest

254

and he plunged into the door, dead before he struck the steps.

There were two other policemen in the arresting party—both constables of the Royal Canadian Mounted Police. One started forward to help Bannister as he fell, and while he stood in the door, Dan reloaded and shot him in the chest.

The third man was Constable Gladwyn. He was an old hand in the police force, and he knew that it was foolhardy to charge a crazy man. Meanwhile King and several others, including Mrs. King, had come up to see what was happening.

"One more man will have to die," Constable Gladwyn said quietly. "I will go in—and you follow and get him after he shoots."

Mrs. King was dismayed.

"No," she cried. "He won't shoot me—I've talked with him. Let me go in and speak to him!"

"You're crazy," King said roughly. "Get back into our house until this is over."

Mrs. King looked at Constable Gladwyn; then she started running toward the shack. The constable shouted, and then started forward, trying to pass her so he could go in first. They reached the shack together, and she stepped through the door.

The big black man was kneeling on the floor, hovering over the body of the dead Indian girl. His rifle lay beside him, and his huge hands were clasped in front of him.

"She done talked!" he said, in a low, hoarse voice. He looked up at the factor's wife. "Missa King—she done talk! God passed a miracle. . . ."

Mrs. King leaned down to see if the girl was dead. Dan did not realize that any other people were in the room until Constable Gladwyn leaned over and snapped a pair of handcuffs around his wrists. He stared wildly at them, but almost immediately his gaze turned downward again to the face of the Indian girl.

"Pore Thela!" he muttered. "She done talk . . . too late."

Dan Williams showed little resistance when the constable hauled him to his feet. Just to make certain that so dangerous a criminal did not escape, the constable tied ropes around his arms.

There was only one moment of excitement. When the Indian girl was buried, he knelt down on her grave, and asked God to let him stay with her. Then, when they tried to pull him away, he fought furiously, knocking people to the ground; but he was still well tied with ropes, and quickly subsided.

He was taken down through the winter snows to Fort Saskatchewan, walking most of the way—shackled and silent. Early in March he was tried in the courtroom at Fort Saskatchewan.

His capture and trial were hailed as a triumph of the forces of law and order in the untamed wilderness where the Hudson's Bay Company spreads its arms. A notorious outlaw had been brought to justice, and the Peace River country was forever liberated from the menace of Nigger Dan.

On the twenty-ninth of March, in the year 1880, Daniel Williams was hanged at Fort Saskatchewan, for the crime of murder.